NATIONAL MAR
QUIZ LEA

D0345670

present

The Martell/RNLI Pub Quiz Book

Max Miller & Chris Lloyd
Wise Owl Quiz Promotions

1,300 brand new questions
from the quiz competition
which raises money for the RNLI

Firebird Books

First published in the United Kingdom in 1993 by
Firebird Books, P.O. Box 327, Poole, Dorset BH15 2RG

ISBN 1 85314 153 4

Typeset by Inforum, Rowlands Castle, Hampshire
Printed and bound in Great Britain by Biddles of Guildford

CONTENTS

INTRODUCTION

The National Martell/RNLI Quiz League is the UK's premier pub quiz competition. Now in it's fourth successful season, the League features hundreds of quiz teams every year from pubs and clubs as far apart as Edinburgh, The Isle of Man and the English South Coast.

Despite being a national competition, all of the leagues are local ones, organised in such a way as to cut down as far as possible excessive travelling to away matches.

The competition not only provides hours of entertainment for thousands of competitors on Monday evenings throughout the winter months, but also raises thousands of pounds for the Lifeboat service, since all of the teams' entry fees go directly to the RNLI.

The finale to the Martell/RNLI Quiz Season is the battle for the coveted *Champion of Champions* title. This takes place every year in Liverpool, on the eve of the Martell Grand National when four of the country's highest scoring League Champions are invited to pit their wits against each other during an all-expenses paid weekend at Aintree.

This book contains 16 complete sets of questions from the National Martell/RNLI Quiz League. The questions cover a wide range of popular and specialist knowledge topics. Each set of questions involves six team rounds of four questions per side, a "specialist" round, an "individual" round, and finally a "gallon" leg which the teams use as a play off for a round of drinks.

You can either use this book informally to test your quiz knowledge against the standard of the competition, or you can use it to run an actual series of quiz matches in your local pub. Complete competition rules are provided, and there is a sample score sheet on page 10 which you can photocopy for each match.

On the following pages we have provided a few ideas for using the questions to run a more ambitious local league or knockout competition involving other teams.

Finally, at the back of the book, you will find full details of how you can enter your team into the next season of the National Martell/RNLI Quiz League, including the Freephone Quizline number for specific enquiries.

Good luck and keep quizzing!

Max Miller and Chris Lloyd
Poole, Dorset
AUGUST 1993

ORGANISING A QUIZ LEAGUE

The ideal number of teams for a quiz league season is eight. If eight teams play each other home and away, the season will involve a total of fourteen matches.

Fewer than eight teams in the league would simply result in a shorter season. Odd numbers of teams should be avoided at all costs, since this would involve at least one team every week not having a match.

More than eight teams in a league becomes slightly cumbersome, and you are better advised to organise two league divisions, each comprising an even number of teams.

The home and away principle ensures that each team's venue has a match every other week – a fair distribution of trade for all concerned.

ORGANISING A KNOCK-OUT COMPETITION

The alternative to a league is a knock out competition. The advantage of this is that you can involve more teams; the disadvantage is that once a team has been eliminated from the competition there is no further interest in it for them.

You can organise four knock out competitions on a sudden death basis for up to sixteen teams using the questions in this book. A more popular alternative is to organise each round of the knock out competition on a two-legged basis, so that each team plays at home and away in order to arrive at an aggregate result.

It is more exciting for the teams involved if you put the names of all the winning teams back into the hat in order to achieve a random draw for the next round, rather than arranging an automatically seeded draw.

Another popular idea is to run a simultaneous "best of the rest" competition for all the first round losers, using the same questions for both competitions. You can do this more than once, depending upon how many teams and rounds you have to play with.

RULES OF THE COMPETITION

1 **MATCH TIMES** The dates, times and venues for all the matches are as indicated on the fixture list issued by the quiz league organiser. Away teams are advised to arrive at the match venue at least fifteen minutes before the stated time, and to advise the opposing team captain of their arrival, since either team can technically claim the game if the opposing team is not ready to begin the game on time (though "claiming the game" would only be done as a last resort.) The quizzes normally last between one and one and a half hours.

2 **TEAMS** Each team needs five members for the match. Four players make up the team to answer the questions, the fifth member acts as the question master at home matches, and the official scorer at away matches. If the team is one player short, then they can recruit any innocent bystander to perform the function of question master/ competitor for them. If the away team is one player short, the scoring can be done by the question master. In any case, the teams are advised to keep their own record of the scoring as the match goes along.

If a team is two or more players short, they can opt to proceed with the match, but they do forfeit automatically the right to answer any of the individual questions for which there are no players. An individual question for a missing player is simply offered to the player opposite for a possible bonus point. (See Rule 6)

The teams should be seated around separate tables so that they can confer quietly outside of earshot of the other side. If possible, the question master should sit between the teams. Both teams should clearly indicate to the question master who their captain is for the night.

It is the responsibility of the home team to provide pencils and scrap paper for both teams to use.

3 **SQUADS** There is no need for players to be "signed on" for the team, or for players to be registered. Teams can draw on as large a squad of players as they can muster, and can "field" different players each week, if they so wish. However, players cannot be substituted

during the course of a match; the team which starts the game must finish it. It is not allowed for players to play for more than one team during the course of the quiz season.

4 QUIZ FORMAT: TEAM QUESTIONS   The question master only accepts answers to questions from the relevant team captain. He does not accept answers shouted out by individual team members. The team should confer, and they should whisper or write down their individual guesses for the captain to choose a team reply. The question master will only accept the captain's first answer.

5 QUIZ FORMAT: THE SPECIALIST SUBJECT ROUND   The rules governing the specialist subject round are exactly as for the other team rounds. At the end of the specialist round the questionmaster will advise both teams what the specialist subject for the next match will be, so that team members may do some research into the subject should they feel so disposed. The specialist subject in the first match in this book is 'The Eurovision Song Contest'.

6 QUIZ FORMAT: INDIVIDUAL QUESTIONS   Round three of the quiz is for the individual team members to answer without conferring with the other players. The captain nominates the order of his team – players 1,2,3 and 4 – (usually clockwise, or from left to right) and it must be clearly established how both teams are numbered before the questions are asked, since if player 1 gives the wrong answer, then it is passed over to player 1 on the other side. No whispering, no writing and no other forms of communication are allowed when players are tackling individual questions. Only the player being asked the question is allowed to use pencil and paper.

7 QUIZ FORMAT: THE "GALLON" LEG   Once the main part of the quiz game is over, the teams play "a gallon". This comprises a set of eight questions per side, and the losers of this part of the quiz have to buy the winning team a round of drinks. The points won in the "gallon" are counted separately from the main quiz. All questions in the "gallon" are team questions.

8 TEAM A/TEAM B   The question master tosses a coin at the beginning of the match to determine which team will play as Team A (i.e. first) or Team B (i.e. second). The away captain is offered the choice of heads or tails. The winner of the toss chooses whether his team is A or B. The teams remain A or B for the whole of the main part of the match – they do not change sides at half time.

At the beginning of the "gallon", the coin is tossed again, and the same procedures are followed.

9 SCORING   The teams are awarded two "quiz" points for a correct answer. If an incorrect answer is given, the question is passed over

to the other side. If they get it right, they win one bonus "quiz" point.

In a league competition, the team with the highest number of "quiz" points at the end of the main part of the match wins two league points. When scores are drawn, each team is awarded one league point. The scores from the "gallon" are counted separately, and again two points are awarded for a win, one point each for a draw.

In the event of a match being forfeited by the non-appearance of the opposing team, the winning team, in claiming the game, shall be awarded 2 league points and a nominal score of 40 "quiz points", plus 2 "gallon" points.

The total number of points scored in the main part of the match is important, since in the case of two teams ending up with the same league points, their respective league positions are determined by their cumulative "quiz points" tally.

In a knock-out cup competition, the total "quiz" points from the main part of the match is the factor which decides who wins and who loses. If an equal number of "quiz" points is scored by both sides, the "gallon" would decide the outcome of the match.

10 TIME   A team, or individual, is allowed 30 seconds to answer the question. The scorer should check the time against a watch, and should advise the relevant captain when 20 seconds have elapsed, and when time is up. When a question is passed over to the other side, only 10 seconds is allowed for them to provide an answer. The question master needs to be strict on the matter of timing, or else the quiz begins to drag out and becomes boring.

11 AUDIENCE INVOLVEMENT   In the event of neither team providing the correct answer to a question, the question master may ask for answers from the floor, simply to keep the audience involved in the game. However, the audience are expected to remain silent during the remainder of the quiz, and if any answers are whispered or shouted by the audience, the question master must remind them of this fact.

12 SPARE QUESTIONS   Each set of quiz questions contains four "spares" to be used in any of the following circumstances:

   A If an answer has been deliberately shouted out from the audience, thereby critically affecting the course of the match.

   B If there is a valid dispute about any of the questions which the question master feels he or she cannot resolve.

   C If the question master has made a mistake in asking the question, which has resulted in the answer being given away.

Remember there are only four spare questions, so use them sparingly.

13 THE QUESTION MASTER'S ROLE   The question master is expected to remain impartial at all times, and to be able to adjudicate in the event of any dispute. He or she must seek the specific answer featured

on the quiz sheet, but must also use his or her own discretion in determining whether an answer is close enough to be acceptable. If faced with a vague or partial reply, he or she can ask for more information. On quiz night, the question master's ruling is final.

The question master is also responsible for ensuring that the quiz is fun, both for those playing and those watching.

14 DISPUTES   An unresolved dispute must be explained in writing to the quiz organiser no later than three days following the match. Disputes should only be pursued when the actual result of the quiz may have been materially affected.

Unresolved disputes can be referred for an impartial adjudication to Wise Owl Quiz Promotions, whose ruling in all matters is final.

15 RESULTS   The responsibility for returning the completed score sheet to the local quiz organiser is the winning team's, or in the case of a draw, the home team's. In any case, the organisers must be notified of match results and final scores by no later than three days following the match.

NATIONAL MARTELL/RNLI QUIZ LEAGUE

SCORE SHEET FOR THE MATCH DATED

THE MAIN QUIZ	THE 'GALLON'

AFTER TOSSING A COIN, THE TEAMS ARE:

TEAM A ....   TEAM B ....

ROUND ONE

	TEAM A		TEAM B	
	POINTS	BONUS	POINTS	BONUS
Q1				
Q2				
Q3				
Q4				
TOTAL				

ROUND TWO

	TEAM A		TEAM B	
	POINTS	BONUS	POINTS	BONUS
Q1				
Q2				
Q3				
Q4				
TOTAL				

RUNNING TOTAL } TEAM A _____ TEAM B _____

ROUND THREE

	TEAM A		TEAM B	
	POINTS	BONUS	POINTS	BONUS
Q1				
Q2				
Q3				
Q4				
TOTAL				

RUNNING TOTAL } TEAM A _____ TEAM B _____

ROUND FOUR

	TEAM A		TEAM B	
	POINTS	BONUS	POINTS	BONUS
Q1				
Q2				
Q3				
Q4				
TOTAL				

HALF TIME SCORE } TEAM A _____ TEAM B _____

ROUND FIVE

	TEAM A		TEAM B	
	POINTS	BONUS	POINTS	BONUS
Q1				
Q2				
Q3				
Q4				
TOTAL				

RUNNING TOTAL } TEAM A _____ TEAM B _____

ROUND SIX

	TEAM A		TEAM B	
	POINTS	BONUS	POINTS	BONUS
Q1				
Q2				
Q3				
Q4				
TOTAL				

RUNNING TOTAL } TEAM A _____ TEAM B _____

ROUND SEVEN

	TEAM A		TEAM B	
	POINTS	BONUS	POINTS	BONUS
Q1				
Q2				
Q3				
Q4				
TOTAL				

RUNNING TOTAL } TEAM A _____ TEAM B _____

FINAL ROUND

	TEAM A		TEAM B	
	POINTS	BONUS	POINTS	BONUS
Q1				
Q2				
Q3				
Q4				
TOTAL				

FINAL SCORE } TEAM A _____ TEAM B _____

THE WINNING TEAM IS ....

THE 'GALLON'

AFTER TOSSING A COIN, THE TEAMS ARE:

TEAM A ....

TEAM B ....

'GALLON' ROUND

	TEAM A		TEAM B	
	POINTS	BONUS	POINTS	BONUS
Q1				
Q2				
Q3				
Q4				
Q5				
Q6				
Q7				
Q8				
TOTAL				

THE WINNER OF THE 'GALLON' ROUND IS ....

THE RESPONSIBILITY FOR RETURNING THIS SCORE SHEET TO YOUR LEAGUE ORGANISER IS THE WINNING TEAM'S OR IN THE CASE OF A DRAW, THE HOME TEAM'S.

THIS SCORE SHEET MUST BE RECEIVED BY YOUR LOCAL LEAGUE ORGANISER WITHIN THREE DAYS OF THE MATCH.

SET OF QUESTIONS FOR MATCH NO. 1

ROUND ONE: TEAM QUESTIONS

TEAM A

Q1: In Ireland, what is the Garda?

Q2: What "animal" is featured on the logo of the Midland Bank?

Q3: Horse Racing. Which company sponsored the 1991 Derby?

Q4: This Scottish nobleman was second husband of Mary Queen of Scots and father of James I of England. He was assassinated in 1567, Who was he?

TEAM B

Q1: In Britain, what is the B.M.A.?

Q2: What "animal" is used on the logo of The National & Provincial Building Society?

Q3: Which horse won the 1991 Derby?

Q4: Born in 1898, this man was premier of the People's Republic of China from 1949 until his death in 1976. Who was he?

ROUND TWO: TEAM QUESTIONS

TEAM A

Q1: In TV's "Doctor Who", which planet did The Daleks come from?

Q2: Who captained HMS Revenge at the defeat of the Spanish Armada in 1588?

Q3: Who was annointed Archbishop of Canterbury on 19th April 1991?

Q4: By what name is Samuel Langhorne Clemens better known?

TEAM B

Q1: In TV's "Doctor Who", which planet did The Ice Warriors come from?

Q2: In which U.S. State is the Grand Canyon to be found?

Q3: Who immediately preceded George Carey as Archbishop of Canterbury?

Q4: What was Bing Crosby's real Christian name?

ROUND THREE: INDIVIDUAL QUESTIONS

TEAM A

Q1: What do the initials G.C. stand for after the name of Malta?

Q2: What was comedian Bernie Winters' St. Bernard dog called?

Q3: In which English County is Clacton-on-Sea?

Q4: Who drives a car with the registration J 1610?

TEAM B

Q1: By what name was Ethiopia previously known?

Q2: In recent by-elections, which "political party" has been represented by Miss Lindi St. Clair?

Q3: In which English County is Catterick?

Q4: Which area of Belgium was contested during the 1944 Battle of the Bulge?

ROUND FOUR: TEAM QUESTIONS

TEAM A

Q1: Which novelist wrote "The Lives and Loves of a She-Devil"?

Q2: Which brewer is based at The Sheaf Brewery, Sheffield?

Q3: What is the B.A.O.R.?

Q4: Which female tennis player has been dubbed "The Whizz-Bang Kid"?

TEAM B

Q1: Which specific activity does the charity LYNX campaign against?

Q2: Which brewer is based at Masham, near Ripon, North Yorkshire?

Q3: In the Army, what is the H.A.C.?

Q4: What nationality is the Rugby League star Greg Austin?

HALF TIME

ROUND FIVE: TEAM QUESTIONS

TEAM A

Q1: Which American car manufacturer bought 50% of the Swedish firm SAAB in 1989?

Q2: St. Swithin's Day falls in which calendar month?

Q3: At which athletics event is the Dream Mile run?

TEAM B

Q1: Name either of the two car manufacturers with which VOLVO have struck a financial and manufacturing alliance?

Q2: Swithin was Bishop of which English Diocese when he died in 852 AD?

Q3: Who is the youngest American athlete ever to compete for the USA team?

Q4: Which writer's real name was Georges Remi?

Q4: Within which country's borders does the bulk of the Kalahari Desert lie?

ROUND SIX: TEAM QUESTIONS

TEAM A

Q1: In Higher Education, what is U.M.I.S.T?

Q2: In which U.S. State is the city of Milwaukee to be found?

Q3: WHAT CENTURY? Chaucer is writing poetry; Robert the Bruce is defeating the English; Tamburlaine is conquering Asia.

Q4: Near which Scottish city is the site of the Battle of Culloden?

TEAM B

Q1: In Higher Education, what is M.I.T.?

Q2: In which U.S. State is the city of Baltimore to be found?

Q3: WHAT CENTURY? Wenceslas, King of Bohemia reigns; the Norsemen discover Greenland; the Vikings defeat the English at the Battle of Malden.

Q4: In T.S. Eliot's poem "Wasteland", which is the cruelest month?

ROUND SEVEN: THE SPECIALIST ROUND
TEAM QUESTIONS ON THE EUROVISION SONG CONTEST

TEAM A

Q1: What was the title of the 1959 U.K. entry, performed by Pearl Carr and Teddy Johnson?

Q2: Who was the U.K.'s female performer in 1970, the year when Dana won the contest for Ireland?

Q3: What was the title of Cliff Richard's 1973 entry, which won second place in the Contest?

Q4: After drawn scores, which nation was deemed to have come second in the 1991 Contest?

TEAM B

Q1: Who sang the U.K.'s 1961 entry, "Are You Sure"?

Q2: Israel won the contest twice, in 1978 and 1979. Name either of the two Israeli performers.

Q3: How many other countries tied with the U.K. when Lulu "won" in 1969?

Q4: Up to, and including 1993, how many U.K. winners have there been?

NOTE: THE SPECIALIST SUBJECT IN THE NEXT MATCH WILL BE BRAM STOKER'S "DRACULA".

FINAL ROUND: TEAM QUESTIONS

TEAM A

Q1: In which modern country would you find native Peloponesians?

Q2: Parts of which two counties were used in 1974 to make up the new English county of Avon?

Q3: What is "Euskada ta Askatasuna"?

Q4: How many times have Brazil won the FIFA World Cup Competition?

TEAM B

Q1: What is the national airline of Greece called?

Q2: Parts of which two counties were used in 1974 to make up the new English county of Cleveland?

Q3: Which British bird is sometimes called the "Redcap" because of its little red face?

Q4: Who did Brazil beat in the 1962 FIFA World Cup Final?

END OF MAIN QUIZ

THE "GALLON" LEG: TEAM QUESTIONS

TEAM A

Q1: Which African country was known until 1975 as Dahomey?

Q2: Name the two men responsible in 1848 for the writing of the Communist Manifesto?

Q3: What is a "palimpsest"?

Q4: Who wrote a book concerning animals, entitled "If Only They Could Talk"?

Q5: What is the derivation of the name of Palestine?

Q6: What do you call a line on map linking points of equal temperature?

Q7: Tenis. Who was mens' singles Champion at Wimbledon in 1974?

TEAM B

Q1: What exactly is Damson Cheese?

Q2: What, according to legend, was "The Holy Grail"?

Q3: Spell "Convalescence"

Q4: What relation is the novelist Margaret Drabble to the 1990 Booker Prize winner A.S. Byatt?

Q5: After Solomon's death, the Kingdom of Israel was split into two – Israel in the north and what in the south?

Q6: Chris Diford and Glen Tilbrook were the songwriting members of which 1980's pop group?

Q7: Boxing. Which Heavyweight Champion was nicknamed "The Cinderella Man"?

Q8: If a person from London is a Londoner, what name is given to a person from Los Angeles?

Q8: Which is the world's largest freshwater lake?

SPARE QUESTIONS FOR USE IN CASE OF MISTAKE OR DISPUTE

Q: Which historic book was compiled in 1086?

Q: Who wrote the novel "The Devil Rides Out"?

Q: Which county did the cricketer W.G. Grace play for?

Q: With what is the science of chronometry concerned?

NATIONAL MARTELL/RNLI QUIZ LEAGUE

MARTELL
COGNAC

SET OF QUESTIONS FOR MATCH NO. 2

ROUND ONE: TEAM QUESTIONS

TEAM A

Q1: What is the name of regular series of meetings involving the heads of the world's seven richest industrial countries?

Q2: In sport, what is the S.A.U.C.B.?

Q3: Which is the only ITV company to have survived since the original ITV franchises were issued in 1955?

Q4: Which member of Abba was actually Norwegian, not Swedish-born?

TEAM B

Q1: The original G7 countries were Britain, France, West Germany, USA, Japan . . . and which two others?

Q2: Liverpool FC set a British record when they signed Dean Saunders from Derby County in July '91. What was the transfer fee?

Q3: How did Swedish pop group Abba come by their name?

Q4: On TV, who are Ian and Janet Tuff?

ROUND TWO: TEAM QUESTIONS

TEAM A

Q1: In which English County is Ford Open Prison?

Q2: In the Roman Catholic Church what name is given to the body which elects the Pope?

Q3: Who won the "Best Actress" Oscar in 1991?

TEAM B

Q1: In which English County are the Cotswold Hills mainly located?

Q2: Who in 1535 first translated the *complete* Bible into English?

Q3: Who co-starred with Cathy Bates in the film "Misery"?

Q4: Near which Somerset town was the Battle of Sedgemoor fought in 1685?

Q4: The Americans call this synthetic material "Dacron". By what name is it known in Britain?

ROUND THREE: INDIVIDUAL QUESTIONS

TEAM A

Q1: Which day of the week is "Poet's Day"?

Q2: What is the name of the Mountie who appears in the Labatts' TV advertisements?

Q3: Which tax, introduced in 1965, is based on profit from the sale of an asset?

Q4: Who was the ruler of Palestine at the time of the birth of Jesus Christ?

TEAM B

Q1: In Australian slang, what is a "dunny"?

Q2: Superior, Michigan, Ontario and Erie are four of the Great Lakes. Name the fifth.

Q3: Which element is represented in science by the letters "Au"?

Q4: What is the more popular name for London's "Shaftesbury memorial"?

ROUND FOUR: TEAM QUESTIONS

TEAM A

Q1: On a full colour map of the London Underground, what colour is the Victoria Line?

Q2: Clonmel is the administrative centre of which Irish County?

Q3: In the modern Army, what is the R.R.C.?

Q4: Which Brewer was originally based at the Chiswell Street Brewery in the City of London?

TEAM B

Q1: By what means does the A102 cross the River Thames?

Q2: Dundalk is the administrative centre of which Irish County?

Q3: Which cartoonish created the schoolgirls of St. Trinians?

Q4: Which Brewer is based at the Griffin Brewery, Chiswick, West London?

HALF TIME

ROUND FIVE: TEAM QUESTIONS

TEAM A

Q1: WHAT YEAR? In the Clitheroe Bye-election, the Liberal Democrats defeat the Conservatives; the punk rock group The Clash have their first No. 1 hit; the Welsh Rugby team are hammered 71–8, their worst defeat in history.

Q2: Blind Hughie, Sebastopol, All Fives and Block are all forms of which popular game?

Q3: Who, for forty years, was writer Gertrude Stein's secretary and constant companion?

Q4: Which Beatles' hit single was premiered live on TV before a worldwide audience of 200 million viewers?

TEAM B

Q1: WHAT YEAR? I.R.A. hunger striker Bobby Sands dies; President Sadat of Egypt is assassinated; John Lennon's "Imagine" is a No. 1 hit.

Q2: Which Chinese game's name literally means in English "The Sparrow"?

Q3: Which authoress was the daughter of radical Mary Wolstonecraft and philosopher William Godwin?

Q4: Which of the Beatles played violin on "All You Need Is Love"?

ROUND SIX: TEAM QUESTIONS

TEAM A

Q1: In which U.S. city was Mike Tyson tried for rape during 1992?

Q2: What activity was common to the wartime films "Fires Were Started" and "The Bells Go Down"?

Q3: What do the initials C.M.G. stand for, after a person's name?

Q4: Which former Yugoslavian city is the capital of Croatia?

TEAM B

Q1: Georges Marchais is the leader of which French political party?

Q2: In the wartime propaganda film "Millions Like Us", where did the women work?

Q3: During 1990, where did over fourteen hundred pilgrims die in a tunnel?

Q4: What kind of animal is a bandog?

ROUND SEVEN: THE SPECIALIST ROUND
TEAM QUESTIONS ON BRAM STOKER'S "DRACULA"

TEAM A

Q1: With which character's "diary" does the story begin its narrative?

Q2: In which range of mountains was Castle Dracula located?

TEAM B

Q1: What is the name of Jonathan Harker's fiancée?

Q2: In which English seaside town did Dracula land?

Q3: What was the name of the ship, wrecked off Whitby, which brought Dracula to England?

Q4: Which foreign doctor treats Lucy Westenra prior to her death?

Q3: In the shape of which animal did Dracula escape from the shipwreck?

Q4: Which historic building did Dracula make his home in England?

NOTE: THE SPECIALIST SUBJECT IN THE NEXT MATCH WILL BE THE SUFFRAGETTE MOVEMENT.

FINAL ROUND: TEAM QUESTIONS

TEAM A

Q1: WHO'S THAT LADY? Born Martha Jane Canary in 1852, she was a drunken brawler, a muleskinner, a Pony Express rider, a prostitute and a transvestite.

Q2: The Danish West Indies were sold to the USA in 1917. By what name are they now known?

Q3: What was tennis star Billy Jean King's maiden name?

Q4: On which river does the Venezuelan port of Ciudad Bolivar stand?

TEAM B

Q1: WHO'S THAT LADY? Born in Italy in 1820, she was 32 when she chose a "dirty menial immodest job" which made her famous, and turned her into a legend of charity and loving care.

Q2: What is Conchology?

Q3: Cullen Skink is Scottish fish soup. What does the word "Cullen" indicate?

Q4: In a military sense, what did the abbreviation C.I.G.S. formerly stand for?

END OF MAIN QUIZ

THE "GALLON" LEG: TEAM QUESTIONS

TEAM A

Q1: Who sang the theme song for the TV series "Auf Weidersehen, Pet" entitled "That's Living All Right"?

Q2: Which English quarter day comes between Mid Summer and Christmas?

Q3: In the 1965 film "The Agony and the Ecstasy", which actor portrayed Pope Julius II"?

TEAM B

Q1: Who took "Snot Rap" into the Top 10 singles charts in 1983?

Q2: Whose official residence is No. 12 Downing Street?

Q3: Which actress portrayed Agatha Christie in the 1978 film "Agatha"?

Q4: What is the official name of the organisation usually referred to as Christian Scientists?

Q4: Which voluntary Anglican organisation was founded in 1882 to assist the parish clergy?

Q5: Who plays "Spenser" in the American TV Detective series "Spenser For Hire"?

Q5: Which FBI Agent does Robert Loggia portray in the American TV Detective series which bears the character's name?

Q6: How did boxer Rocky Marciano die?

Q6: What is the female equivalent of a Venture Scout, for girls over 16 years old?

Q7: What was the name of the astronaut who first hit a golf ball on the Moon?

Q7: What rank did Phil Silvers' character "Bilko" attain in the U.S. Army?

Q8: On which U.S. river does the city of Cincinnati stand?

Q8: Which were the last Olympic Games in which South Africa participated before being banned by the I.O.C. because of apartheid?

SPARE QUESTIONS
FOR USE IN CASE OF MISTAKE OR DISPUTE

Q: What is the meaning of the world "circumsolar"?

Q: How many cents are there in one dime?

Q: What is the official name or title of the organisation we usually refer to as the "Mormons"?

Q: How many children did Queen Victoria bear?

SET OF QUESTIONS FOR MATCH NO. 3

ROUND ONE: TEAM QUESTIONS

TEAM A

Q: Which famous architect was born in the Wiltshire village of East Knoyle?

Q2: In which country would you find the 145 mile long Gota Canal?

Q3: Which, by area, is the largest post-1974 English County?

Q4: What is cupro-nickel?

TEAM B

Q1: Which architect designed the new Coventry Cathedral, consecrated in 1962?

Q2: In which country would you find the 80 mile long Albert Canal?

Q3: Which, by area, is the smallest post-1974 English County?

Q4: How many old (pre-decimal) penny coins weighed one ounce?

ROUND TWO: TEAM QUESTIONS

TEAM A

Q1: What was the Royal Shakespeare Company Theatre at Stratford called from 1870 until it was renamed in the 1960's?

Q2: In which U.S. State is the city of Wichita to be found?

Q3: Which actor was "Monty's Double" both on film and in real life?

Q4: Near which modern North African city do the ruins of Carthage lie?

TEAM B

Q1: Which new Bank Holiday was introduced in England in 1975?

Q2: Kansas City straddles the border of two U.S. States – one is Kansas, which is the other?

Q3: Which two nations contested the Punic Wars?

Q4: Name either of the two alcoholic drinks used to make a "Cold Duck" cocktail

ROUND THREE: INDIVIDUAL QUESTIONS

TEAM A

Q1: Which flag was nicknamed "The Stars and Bars"?

Q2: Who directed the 1979 film "Alien"?

Q3: Which English County played first class cricket for the first time in 1992?

Q4: In which modern English County is Great Yarmouth?

TEAM B

Q1: Which dance craze did pop act Kaoma introduce to the British music charts in 1989?

Q2: What insect is kept in a vespiary?

Q3: In which modern English County is Weston-super-Mare?

Q4: In the 1960 film "The Alamo", which historical character did Richard Widmark portray?

ROUND FOUR: TEAM QUESTIONS

TEAM A

Q1: Who flies the flag known as the Blue Ensign?

Q2: In aviation history, which aircraft was the E28–39?

Q3: In finance, what is C.T.T.?

Q4: Which female journalist was appointed Editor of the Sunday Express in May 1991?

TEAM B

Q1: Which two colours are featured on the flag of St. Patrick?

Q2: Who was the first pilot to fly an aircraft at Mach 1 speed?

Q3: Which football club's supporters' fanzine is called "Monkey Business"

Q4: In Higher Education, what is the C.N.A.A.?

HALF TIME

ROUND FIVE: TEAM QUESTIONS

TEAM A

Q1: WHAT CENTURY? King Edward II is murdered (in horrible circumstances); the English beat the French at the Battle of Crecy; Wat Tyler leads The Peasants' Revolt.

Q2: In the world of P.G. Wodehouse, which of Bertie Wooster's pals was renowned for keeping pet newts?

TEAM B

Q1: WHAT CENTURY? Simon de Montfort leads the Revolt of the Barons; Wales is finally conquered by the English; the Japanese repulse the Mongol invasion.

Q2: To which London Club did Bertie Wooster and his chums belong?

Q3: According to the Chinese Calendar, which animal governs the year 1993?

Q4: On which New York street is the Empire State Building to be found?

Q3: What does the prefix "photo" indicate in a word?

Q4: On which New York street is the 77-storey high Chrysler Building to be found?

ROUND SIX: TEAM QUESTIONS

TEAM A

Q1: What was the title of Jilted John's 1978 Top Ten hit single?

Q2: In Australian slang, what is "underground mutton"

Q3: Which mineral is mined at Burra Burra, South Australia?

Q4: How many V.C.s were awarded as a result of the 1991 Gulf War?

TEAM B

Q1: Which pianist had a "Walk in the Black Forest" back in 1965?

Q2: To an Australian, what is a "ten-ounce sandwich"?

Q3: Which disaffected people strive to create their own state, called Kalistan?

Q4: Name either of the two television news reporters who were awarded civil decorations, as a result of their work during the Gulf War?

ROUND SEVEN: THE SPECIALIST ROUND
TEAM QUESTIONS ON THE SUFFRAGETTE MOVEMENT

TEAM A

Q1: Emmeline Pankhurst bore two daughters, both of whom were involved in the suffragette movement. What were their names?

Q2: Whilst attending marches and rallies, the Suffragettes wore "Battle Dresses" comprising three different colours. What were the colours?

Q3: For what crime did Emmeline Pankhurst receive three years imprisonment?

Q4: Which Act of Parliament in 1918 gave the vote only to women over the age of 30?

TEAM B

Q1: What was the official title of the Suffragette movement?

Q2: In May 1914, Mrs Pankhurst was arrested outside Buckingham Palace. For what reason?

Q3: What was the name of the Oxford graduate who died after throwing herself under King George V's horse at the 1913 Epsom Derby?

Q4: In 1928, the Equal Franchise Act extended the vote to all women over what age?

NOTE: THE SPECIALIST SUBJECT IN THE NEXT MATCH WILL BE THE BBC RADIO SOAP OPERA "THE ARCHERS".

FINAL ROUND: TEAM QUESTIONS

TEAM A

Q1: Who wrote the 1991 T.V. drama series "G.B.H."

Q2: Spell "etymological"

Q3: Who, in 1990, was the first British woman to win the British Open Squash Championship in thirty years?

Q4: Which of the stellar constellations is "The Dragon"?

TEAM B

Q1: Which T.V. legal drama series stars actors Harry Hamlin and Susan Dey?

Q2: Spell "eucharist" (Pronounced yoo-karrist)

Q3: Who (up to 1993) has been the only female British squash player to have been Champion of the World?

Q4: Which of the stellar constellations is "The Swan"?

END OF MAIN QUIZ

THE "GALLON" LEG: TEAM QUESTIONS

TEAM A

Q1: WHO'S THAT LADY? IN 1920 she was the hottest name in fashion; Yves St. Laurent called her "the Godmother of us all"; she died in 1971.

Q2: Who was the Poet Laureate immediately before Ted Hughes?

Q3: Which country's civil aircraft carry the registration letters PH?

Q4: Which singer, nicknamed "The Godfather of Soul", wrote the classic soul song "Papa's Got A Brand New Bag"?

Q5: Where, in 1930, was Princess Margaret born?

Q6: From what metal is The George Cross made?

TEAM B

Q1: WHO'S THAT LADY? An actress, she died in 1962. Billy Wilder said "she had breasts like granite and a brain like Swiss cheese, full of holes".

Q2: Which poet stated his work was concerned with "war, and the pity of war"?

Q3: Which country's civil aircraft carry the registration letters N, or NC?

Q4: Which legendary American rock 'n' roll guitarist, real name Charlie Westover, committed suicide in February 1990?

Q5: Where in 1950 was Princess Anne born?

Q6: What words are used as the inscription on The George Cross?

Q7: Which sportsman's daughter married Raquel Welch's son in June 1991?

Q8: Who, in mythology, founded the city of Rome?

Q7: Which actress is the mother of TV presenter Jenny Hanley?

Q8: In Ancient Rome, if the plebeians were the common people, who were the nobility?

SPARE QUESTIONS
FOR USE IN CASE OF MISTAKE OR DISPUTE

Q: What was the name of Mao Tse Tung's widow, the leader of the Gang of Four, who "committed suicide" in 1991?

Q: Which English poet, born 1772, died 1834, wrote "Kubla Khan" and "Christabel"?

Q: Which body of representatives from Church and State administers the endowments and property of The Church of England?

Q: What was Scotland called in Macbeth's day?

SET OF QUESTIONS FOR MATCH NO. 4

ROUND ONE: TEAM QUESTIONS

TEAM A

Q1: To a train spotter, what does the term "pre-Grouping" mean?

Q2: Which Elizabethan dramatist wrote "Volpone" and "The Alchemist"?

Q3: Who is the popular Conservative M.P. for Macclesfield, Cheshire?

Q4: In which year did Roald Amundsen become the first man to reach the South Pole?

TEAM B

Q1: To a train spotter, what is the significance of the number 4468?

Q2: Which Elizabethan dramatist wrote "The White Devil" and "The Duchess of Malfi"?

Q3: Who is the highly respected Labour M.P. for Leicester East?

Q4: How did explorer Roald Amundsen die, in 1928?

ROUND TWO: TEAM QUESTIONS

TEAM A

Q1: How many clubs started the 1991–1992 English Football League season?

Q2: Which British pop promoter of the 1950s invented the stage names Marty Wilde, Billy Fury and Georgie Fame for his pop stars?

Q3: In the Bible, which woman was the wife of Abraham?

Q4: What is a "Cep"?

TEAM B

Q1: Which pop musician's real name is Clive Powell?

Q2: According to The Book of Genesis, whom did God order Abraham to sacrifice as a test of faith?

Q3: Who uses "Oofle Dust" to perform his "magic tricks"?

Q4: Axl Rose is the assumed name of which rock band's lead singer?

ROUND THREE: INDIVIDUAL QUESTIONS

TEAM A

Q1: Who is the host of the TV programme "Saturday Night Clive"?

Q2: From which prison did I.R.A. suspects Pearse McAuley and Nessan Quinlivan escape in July 1991?

Q3: Who composed "The Dream of Gerontius"?

Q4: During which month of 1940 did the evacuation of Dunkirk begin?

TEAM B

Q1: Which Argentine President ordered the invasion of the Falkland Islands in 1982?

Q2: In British military history, which battle lasted 82 days, from 10th July to 31st October?

Q3: Who portrayed Tchaikovsky in Ken Russell's film "The Music Lovers"?

Q4: What is the title of Roy Clark's TV comedy series about a mean Northern shopkeeper?

ROUND FOUR: TEAM QUESTIONS

TEAM A

Q1: Who is the youngest ever woman to win the French Open Tennis Championship?

Q2: What title did archaeologist Sir John Lubbock adopt upon his elevation to the peerage?

Q3: Which music hall performer attracted 100,000 people to her funeral in 1922?

Q4: Following which 1974 I.R.A. bomb attack was Judith Ward jailed?

TEAM B

Q1: If the New Stone Age was called the Neolithic, what was the Old Stone Age called?

Q2: Which French physicist discovered radioactivity in 1896?

Q3: Following which I.R.A. bomb attack in 1974 were the "McGuire Seven" jailed?

Q4: An organisation called the BSSAA has recently opened up a telephone helpline to help people sleep better. What specific problem do they tackle?

HALF TIME

ROUND FIVE: TEAM QUESTIONS

TEAM A

Q1: The old Welsh county of Flint has been absorbed into which modern county?

Q2: Which actor repeated his Broadway triumph in the 1960 film version of "The Music Man"?

TEAM B

Q1: Which town is the administrative centre of the county of Clwyd?

Q2: Which rock group's music is used as the theme tune for BBC TV's "Grand Prix" programme?

Q3: Which rock group's music is used as the theme tune for BBC TV's "Top Gear" motoring programme?

Q4: In the 1988 World Snooker Championship, two players competed in a second round match where the average duration of each frame was only 11 minutes. Name either player.

Q3: How many times has the World Professional Snooker Championship been won by players from beyond the British Isles?

Q4: Who starred opposite Yul Brunner in the 1956 film version of the musical "The King and I"?

ROUND SIX: TEAM QUESTIONS

TEAM A

Q1: In which of Shakespeare's plays does the character "Ariel" appear?

Q2: During the American Civil War by what nickname was General Joseph Hooker known as?

Q3: In which French Region does Camembert cheese originate?

Q4: Ruby is the traditional birthstone of which calendar month?

TEAM B

Q1: Which Christian action group, famous for its prolific publishing activity, was founded in Wisconsin in 1899?

Q2: On which London Underground line would you find The Oval station?

Q3: What distinguishes "fromage de chevre" from other cheeses?

Q4: Topaz or Amber are the traditional birthstones for which calendar month?

ROUND SEVEN: THE SPECIALIST ROUND TEAM QUESTIONS ON THE BBC RADIO SOAP OPERA "THE ARCHERS"

TEAM A

Q1: Which member of the Royal Family made a guest appearance on "The Archers" in 1984?

Q2: Who lives at Nightingale Farm?

Q3: With whom did Kathy Perks have an extra-marital affair during the course of 1990?

Q4: Which Ambridge location is haunted by the ghost of "Black Lawson"?

TEAM B

Q1: Which political party did Mark Hebden represent on the local council until his resignation in 1988?

Q2: Who is the actual licensee of "The Bull"?

Q3: Who lives at Home Farm?

Q4: To which saint is the Parish Church of Ambridge dedicated?

FINAL ROUND: TEAM QUESTIONS

TEAM A

Q1: What is colloquially referred to as "the Tartan Curtain"?

Q2: Traces of which chemical caused Perrier Water to be withdrawn from sale during 1990?

Q3: Why was a dog called "Rinker" making front page news in 1979?

Q4: In 1985, Ramiz Alia became the President of which East European country?

TEAM B

Q1: Which wedding anniversary is celebrated with turquoise or tin?

Q2: Who is the leader of the Afrikaaner Resistance Movement (the "A.W.B.")?

Q3: Which gardening implement did Edwin Budding invent in 1830?

Q4: What do the initials B.S.B. now stand for?

END OF MAIN QUIZ

THE "GALLON" LEG: TEAM QUESTIONS

TEAM A

Q1: What is the date of the feast of St. Nicholas?

Q2: Which major golf tournament during 1991 was held at Crooked Stick, Indiana?

Q3: Sir Jack Lyons was fined three million pounds during 1990. Why?

Q4: What product was the subject of the first ever advertisement on British Independent Television?

Q5: WHAT CENTURY? Printing was introduced in Europe; Constantinople was taken by the Turks; the Moors were driven back to Africa by the Spanish.

Q6: Which Independent Local Radio Station is based in Edinburgh?

TEAM B

Q1: What is the date of the feast of St. Stephen?

Q2: Who managed West Germany's football World Cup Squad in 1986?

Q3: What now obsolete world describes the collective body of Christians throughout the world or throughout history?

Q4: Born Mark Feld in London in 1947, by what name did this pop star become better known?

Q5: WHAT CENTURY? Robert Emmet starts an insurrection in Ireland; Argentina is the first South American state to become independent of Spain; The Monroe Doctrine announced by the U.S.A.

Q6: In which Scottish city is Radio Moray Firth based?

Q7: Who wrote the screenplay for the classic 1945 film "Brief Encounter"?

Q7: Who directed the 1945 film "Brief Encounter"?

Q8: Which man organised (in 1941) the world's first package holiday?

Q8: What was the family name of the First Duke of Marlborough?

SPARE QUESTIONS
FOR USE IN CASE OF MISTAKE OR DISPUTE

Q: Tarquin the Proud was the last King of . . . where?

Q: In the BBC Radio series "The Archers", what are the christian names of Peggy Woolley's three children?

Q: Which common Christmas item was described by Charles Dickens in 1850 as "this new German toy"?

Q: What is the principal monetry unit of Peru?

SET OF QUESTIONS FOR MATCH NO. 5

ROUND ONE: TEAM QUESTIONS

TEAM A

Q1: On which island did St. Paul spend three months in A.D. 60 after being shipwrecked?

Q2: Which is the smallest of all species of Penguin?

Q3: Which country has been ruled by Fahd ibn Abd al-Aziz since 1982?

Q4: Which World Champion Motor Racing Champion was once held hostage by Castro's revolutionaries in Cuba?

TEAM B

Q1: In the world of classical music what is Lorin Maazel famous as?

Q2. Which Welsh city, centre of the Ceredigion district, stands on the mouths of the Ystwyth and Rheidol rivers?

Q3: With which sport do you associate Hank Aaron?

Q4: What is a "coney"?

ROUND TWO: TEAM QUESTIONS

TEAM A

Q1: Which TV serial features the minor characters Phil Jennings and Reg Holdsworth?

Q2: What is a "macadamia", when eaten?

Q3: Which Biblical character, and brother of Moses, was the first High Priest of the Israelites?

TEAM B

Q1: Which TV drama series features the characters Duffy, Megan, and Charlie Fairhead?

Q2: Off the coast of which European country is the holiday island of Rab to be found?

Q3: What name is given to a story about animals, which can be interpreted as referring to human behaviour?

Q4: What kind of animal is a macaque?

Q4: In the Bible, which wife of Jacob was mother of Joseph and Benjamin?

ROUND THREE: INDIVIDUAL QUESTIONS

TEAM A

Q1: From which country did the fandango dance originate?

Q2: What is the name of Inspector Morse's faithful assistant?

Q3: Which film company created the series of movies featuring "Herbie" the car with a mind of its own?

Q4: What two colours are featured on the flag of the United Nations?

TEAM B

Q1: Which writer created the character Chief Inspector Wexford?

Q2: On a weekday, at what time is Channel Four's evening news programme broadcast?

Q3: Which General led the Allied forces which recaptured the South West Pacific between 1942 and 1945?

Q4: Which building was the Citadel of ancient Athens?

ROUND FOUR: TEAM QUESTIONS

TEAM A

Q1: Which Scottish city was called "Devana" in ancient times?

Q2: What name is given to the arrangement when a Company sells its complete debtors list to an agent for retrieval?

Q3: Which Australian actor starred in the 1982 movie "Far East"?

Q4: The membership of The National Trust voted in 1990 to ban which blood sport on its land?

TEAM B

Q1: Which city marks the Alaskan terminus of the Alaskan Railway?

Q2: Which famous religious leader's uncle was called Abbas, and became the chief promoter of his faith?

Q3: Which English actor starred in the 1946 film "Anna and The King of Siam"?

Q4: Which woman was elected President of the Irish Republic during 1990?

HALF TIME

ROUND FIVE: TEAM QUESTIONS

TEAM A

Q1: Which nation governs the Faeroe Islands?

TEAM B

Q1: Where in the British Isles is the Abbey Theatre to be found?

Q2: Which Socialist political group founded in 1884 took its name from a Roman General famed for his cautious tactics?

Q3: In the 1991 World Student Games in Sheffield, which nation won the most medals?

Q4: In which radio quiz show is the question setter, Ian Gillies, referred to as "Mycroft" by the questionmaster?

Q2: Which city was the capital of Charlemagne's Holy Roman Empire?

Q3: In the 1991 World Student Games, which gold medal winning athlete was the captain of the British team?

Q4: How does a rider refer to the left hand side of the horse?

ROUND SIX: TEAM QUESTIONS

TEAM A

Q1: You've heard of the Y.M.C.A. but what is the Y.M.H.A.?

Q2: What is an abalone?

Q3: What is writer Hugh MacDiarmid mainly renowned for?

Q4: From which Football Club did Napoli sign Diego Maradona for £5 million in 1984?

TEAM B

Q1: Which religious organisation is the W.C.C.?

Q2: Where in the human body would you find "Factor 8"?

Q3: Who composed the ballet entitled the "Three Cornered Hat"?

A4: From which Football League Club did Everton sign Tony Cottee in 1988?

ROUND SEVEN: THE SPECIALIST ROUND
TEAM QUESTIONS ON THE BURGESS-MACLEAN-PHILBY SPY SCANDAL

TEAM A

Q1: What was the name of the Society at Cambridge University through which Blunt, MacLean, Burgess and Philby developed their Marxist ideas?

Q2: Give either of the Intelligence Service's codenames for the (then) unknown Fourth and Fifth men in the consiracy

Q3: Who was the head of the British Secret Service, known as "C", from 1931 to 1952?

TEAM B

Q1: Who was the British Foreign Secretary who cleared Philby of being the "Third Man" in the 1955 Commons debate?

Q2: In which year did Burgess and Maclean defect?

Q3: From which city did Philby disappear in 1963, in his defection to the Russians?

Q4: To which key post was Philby promoted in 1949?

Q4: How did Burgess and Maclean escape from England in 1951?

NOTE: THE SPECIALIST SUBJECT IN THE NEXT MATCH WILL BE THE TOUR DE FRANCE.

FINAL ROUND: TEAM QUESTIONS

TEAM A

Q1: In which West African country is the seaport of Abidjan?

Q2: According to Shakespeare, which King of Scotland did Lady Macbeth murder?

Q3: What is a "ragged robin"?

Q4: In which modern Welsh county is the coal mining village of Aberfan to be found?

TEAM B

Q1: In which country is the city of Faisalbad?

Q2: According to Shakespeare, who killed Macbeth?

Q3: What kind of animal is the falabella the smallest species on earth?

Q4: What colour is the cross on the national flag of Denmark?

END OF MAIN QUIZ

THE "GALLON" LEG: TEAM QUESTIONS

TEAM A

Q1: Who succeeded Sayed Ali Khamenei as President of Iran in 1989?

Q2: Which of Canada's Provinces was the last to join the Union in 1948?

Q3: Who was the legendary lover of the theologian Peter Abelard?

Q4: Which country has the international car registration letters "TG"?

Q5: Who wrote the novel "All Quiet on the Western Front"?

TEAM B

Q1: Which collection of writings do you find (in some Bibles) between the Old and New Testaments?

Q2: The Canadian Pacific Railroad stretches from Halifax in the east to which west coast city?

A3: Which German physicist invented the alcohol thermometer?

Q4: Which country has the international car registration letters "PA"?

Q5: Who wrote the novel "From Here to Eternity"?

Q6: Name the only Canadian ever to have held the title of World Heavyweight Boxing Champion.

Q7: Who was the first British King to hold the title "Emperor of India"?

Q8: Which pop group wanted it to be "Perfect" in 1988?

Q6: Who took Mike Tyson's World Heavyweight title from him in 1990?

Q7: Who succeeded George The Fourth as British Monarch in 1830?

Q8: Whose "judicial" cover version of "Je T'aime Moi Non Plus" was a hit record in 1975?

SPARE QUESTIONS
FOR USE IN CASE OF MISTAKE OR DISPUTE

Q: What is a "fairy bluebird"?

Q: What is 'achondroplasia"?

Q: From hich country does "raga" music originate?

Q: After 1975, tho African country known previously as Dahomey has been called what?

SET OF QUESTIONS FOR MATCH NO. 6

ROUND ONE: TEAM QUESTIONS
A GENERAL KNOWLEDGE ROUND

TEAM A

Q1: When the poet Houseman talked of "blue remembered hills", which English county was he talking of?

Q2: Which (now deceased) disc jockey's autobiography was called "Tomorrow's Too Late"?

Q3: Which Italian composer wrote an opera about William Tell?

Q4: During the 1960s, what was the U.S. Air Force's "Operation Bluebook" concerned with?

TEAM B

Q1: What did the "Burnham Scale" determine?

Q2: In which of Oscar Wilde's plays does Mrs Erlynne cause a scandal in London society?

Q3: Who, at five years old, composed the music for "Twinkle, Twinkle Little Star"?

Q4: When Charles Lindburg flew the Atlantic solo in the "Spirit of St. Louis", in which country did he land?

ROUND TWO: TEAM QUESTIONS
A SPORTING ROUND

TEAM A

Q1: In which sport is Britain's Robert Fulford the World Champion?

Q2: From which Dutch Football Club did AC Milan sign Ruud Gullit in 1987 for £5½ million?

TEAM B

Q1: Which golfer won the 1991 British Open Championship?

Q2: For which national cricket side was R.S. Madugalle the captain, during 1988?

Q3: Which President of FIFA agreed the deal which bestowed the 1994 World Cup upon the U.S.A.?

Q4: What nationality is the former British Open Squash Champion Susan Devoy?

Q3: What item connects the children's games "Squeak Piggy Squeak", "Blind Man's Stick" and "Nelson's Eye"?

Q4: Who is Boris Becker's manager/personal coach?

ROUND THREE: INDIVIDUAL QUESTIONS

TEAM A

Q1: Which river is known as "China's Sorrow"?

Q2: What substance is known as "Texas Tea"?

Q3: In 1950, King Leopold III abdicated from the throne of which country?

Q4: What kind of food is Samsoe?

TEAM B

Q1: What happens in a "velodrome"?

Q2: What is British Honduras now known as?

Q3: What award is made by The European Community to seaside resorts with clean beaches?

Q4: "Patna" is what kind of foodstuff?

ROUND FOUR: TEAM QUESTIONS
A GEOGRAPHICAL ROUND

TEAM A

Q1: In which U.S. State is the city of Buffalo to be found?

Q2: Which neutral Portuguese colony existed in British India during World War II?

Q3: Which country is known as the "cockpit of Europe"?

Q4: What appears in the top left hand corner of the national flag of Malta?

TEAM B

Q1: In which U.S. State is the city of Cincinnati to be found?

Q2: Goa is 500 miles south of which Indian city?

Q3: Which is the most easterly of the Caribbean Islands?

Q4: What colour is the triangle on the national flag of Czechoslovakia?

HALF TIME

ROUND FIVE: TEAM QUESTIONS
AN ENTERTAINMENTS ROUND

TEAM A

Q1: Who directed the 1962 film "Doctor Zivago"?

TEAM B

Q1: Which actress portrayed the heroine, a friendly witch, in the 1971 film "Bedknobs & Broomsticks"?

Q2: Which female TV presenter was seen on our screens with Muffin the Mule?

Q3: Which actor portrayed the TV detective "MacLeod"?

Q4: Which pop singer sang "They're Coming To Take Me Away, Ha Ha" in 1966?

Q2: In which BBC TV series does Neil Patrick Harris portray a teenage hospital doctor?

Q3: How does Radio 1 disc jockey Jakki Brambles spell her christian name?

Q4: Which pop group was "Lonely This Christmas" in 1974?

ROUND SIX: TEAM QUESTIONS
AN HISTORICAL ROUND

TEAM A

Q1: Which 18th Century economist has been dubbed "The Founding Father of Free Trade"?

Q2: Samuel de Champlain founded which Canadian city in 1608?

Q3: What nationality was the great General Hannibal?

Q4: What series of wars was England involved in between 1652 and 1674?

TEAM B

Q1: In 19th Century Japan whose authority was relinquished to the Emperor in the "Meiji Restoration"?

Q2: Which French General opposed Wolfe at The Battle of Quebec in 1759?

Q3: Which Roman General defeated Hannibal, destroyed Carthage, and ended the Punic Wars?

Q4: Which English naval port did the Dutch raid in June 1667?

ROUND SEVEN: THE SPECIALIST ROUND
TEAM QUESTIONS ON THE TOUR DE FRANCE

TEAM A

Q1: In the Tour de France, what colour jersey does the "best newcomer" wear?

Q2: In the road racing stages, what happens when the riders "bonk"?

Q3: How long does the Tour de France last?

Q4: Who was the last Frenchman to win the "Tour" (prior to 1993)?

TEAM B

Q1: The Tour de France comprises three different types of racing – Road Races, Individual Time Trials, and . . . what is the third?

Q2: In the Tour de France, which rider wears a red polka-dot jersey?

Q3: In the Tour de France, what is the "Peloton"?

Q4: Apart from Hinault, name either of the other two riders who have won the "Tour" five times?

FINAL ROUND: TEAM QUESTIONS
A SCIENCE AND NATURE ROUND

TEAM A

Q1: What does a heliologist study?

Q2: Which drug represented the only treatment against malaria until the 1920's?

Q3: Which of the signs of the Zodiac is "The Ram"?

Q4: Which element used to be called "quicksilver"?

TEAM B

Q1: What are the three primary colours of light?

Q2: Which is the second largest planet in the Solar System?

Q3: Which of the signs of the Zodiac is "The Crab"

Q4: Which science is the classification and study of metals?

END OF MAIN QUIZ

THE "GALLON" LEG: TEAM QUESTIONS

TEAM A

Q1: Why were Avro aircraft so-called?

Q2: How are Sara Dallin and Keren Woodward better known?

Q3: Of which European country was Flavio Cotti the President during 1991?

Q4: Why are pink flamingos pink?

Q5: For the independence of which country did Frelimo fight during the 1970's?

Q6: Which of Shakespeare's plays features the character Helen of Troy?

Q7: What is it that the Spanish call OTAN?

Q8: Which is the world's longest railway tunnel?

TEAM B

Q1: If a ship fires a gun at intervals of a minute, what is it signalling?

Q2: What was the name of the Orchestra led by Max Jaffa in the radio programme "Grand Hotel"?

Q3: Of which nation is Lee Teng-hui the current President?

Q4: What is the basic difference between worker bees and drones?

Q5: In nautical terms, what is a "caboose"?

Q6: Which of Shakespeare's plays features the character Fortinbras?

Q7: What type of beer do they sell in "The Bull", Ambridge?

Q8: Which is Britain's longest railway tunnel?

Q: Who wrote "The History of the World" whilst imprisoned in the Tower of London?

Q: In Hardy's Wessex, what real place was called Sandbourne?

Q: Which poet wrote the words to the popular hymn "Jerusalem"?

Q: Which political organisation's name means, in English, "We, ourselves, alone"?

SET OF QUESTIONS FOR MATCH NO. 7

ROUND ONE: TEAM QUESTIONS

TEAM A

Q1: Who won the 1990 Nobel Peace Prize?

Q2: On a clothes label, what does a symbol comprising a circle with a cross through it indicate?

Q3: Which country boasts an airline called "Rottnest"?

Q4: In the world of TV comedy, whose cat was called "Vienna"?

TEAM B

Q1: Which was the last British writer to win the Nobel prize for Literature?

Q2. On a printed form, what does a pair of scissors indicate?

Q3: Which country boasts an airline called "Janair"?

Q4: In "Rising Damp" which actor portrayed the character "Philip"?

ROUND TWO: TEAM QUESTIONS

TEAM A

Q1: Who is the Patron Saint of students and scholars?

Q2: In musical notation, which note is half a "minim"?

Q3: At what sport is Vijay Singh one of the world's top professionals?

Q4: If a man wears a size 8 shoe in Britain what size must he buy on the Continent?

TEAM B

Q1: Who is the Patron Saint of prisoners?

Q2: In musical notation, which note is twice the length of a minim?

Q3: What nationality (not Indian) is golfer Vijay Singh?

Q4: If a woman wears a size 10 dress in Britain, what size must she buy on the Continent?

ROUND THREE: INDIVIDUAL QUESTIONS

TEAM A

Q1: Who is the compere of the TV Quiz Show "Call My Bluff"?

Q2: Which British Formula One racing driver was World Champion in 1973?

Q3: Of which country is Prince Norodom Sihanouk the leader?

Q4: What basic ingredient gives Ouzo its characteristic flavour?

TEAM B

Q1: Which actress starred in the films "Viva Maria" & "And God Created Woman"?

Q2: Which wedding anniversary is celebrated with Diamond?

Q3: Which part of the human biological mechanism defends the body against infections and disease?

Q4: For which organisation was Jill Morrell the spokeswoman from 1988 to 1991?

ROUND FOUR: TEAM QUESTIONS

TEAM A

Q1: What official post connects these names: Shadwell, Tate, Rowe, Eusden, Cibber?

Q2: Which English Football Club has been managed since the War by Tommy Docherty, Colin Addison and Peter Taylor?

Q3: In Chess notation, what does a small diagonal cross (x) indicate?

Q4: Which of the States of the USA is the "Keystone State"?

TEAM B

Q1: Which man succeeded Robert Southey as Poet Laureate?

Q2: Which English Football Club has been managed since the War by Peter Taylor, Alan Mullery and Jimmy Melia?

Q3: In Chess notation what does an exclamation mark indicate?

Q4: Which of the States of the USA is known as the "Mother of Presidents"?

HALF TIME

ROUND FIVE: TEAM QUESTIONS

TEAM A

Q1: The "Prix Goncourt" is France's leading prize in what sphere of activity?

Q2: Which company (or product) sponsors the Admiral's Cup Yacht Race?

TEAM B

Q1: Which of Salman Rushdie's novels won the Booker Pize for Fiction in 1981?

Q2: Where in England was one stage of the World Surfing Championships held in 1991?

Q3: What is the shape of St. Anthony's cross?

Q4: Which actor was "Billy Liar" in the 1963 film of the same name?

Q3: What is the shape of St. Andrew's cross?

Q4: Which actress co-starred with Cliff Richard in the 1964 film "A Wonderful Life"?

ROUND SIX: TEAM QUESTIONS

TEAM A

Q1: In which country were the 1992 Winter Olympic Games held?

Q2: Which river rises on Cross Fell, Cumbria, and flows through Barnard Castle on its way to the north Sea?

Q3: In the TV comedy series, "Last of the Summer Wine", which actor portrays Compo?

Q4: In the Bible, how many of the Ten Commandments are religious, and how many are about social relations?

TEAM B

Q1: In which country were the 1988 Winter Olympic Games held?

Q2: Which river rises in the Pennine Hills, North Yorkshire, and flows through Preston on its way to the Irish Sea?

Q3: Who preceeded Anne Robinson as the regular presenter of BBC TV's "Points of View"?

Q4: In which Book of the Bible would you find the Ten Commandments?

ROUND SEVEN: THE SPECIALIST ROUND
TEAM QUESTIONS ON THE FALKLANDS WAR, 1982

TEAM A

Q1: Who was the British Governor of the Falkland Islands in 1982?

Q2: In which month during 1982 did the British Forces liberate the Falkland Islands?

Q3: What was the ostensible reason for the Argentine scrap merchants landing on South Georgia on March 19th?

Q4: Who led the British Forces which retook Darwin and Goose Green on 28th May?

TEAM B

Q1: In which month during 1982 did the Argentine forces invade the Falkland Islands?

Q2: Name either of the other two Foreign Office Ministers who resigned along with Lord Carrington on April 5th?

Q3: Who commanded the British Task Force which left Portsmouth on April 5th?

Q4: Which U.S. Secretary of State had been conducting peace negotiations up to the point when the Belgrano was sunk?

FINAL ROUND: TEAM QUESTIONS

TEAM A

Q1: Actor Daniel Day Lewis won the Best Actor Oscar in 1989 for his starring role in which film?

Q2: On which London Underground Line would you find Arsenal station?

Q3: In music, what does "forte" mean?

Q4: Which Welsh National Park Area contains the Black Mountains where the S.A.S. train?

TEAM B

Q1: Bruce Beresford won the Best Picture Oscar in 1989 for which film?

Q2: On which London Underground Line would you find West Ham station?

Q3: In music, what does "crescendo" mean?

Q4: Which area was the first officially designated National Park in England and Wales?

END OF MAIN QUIZ

THE "GALLON" LEG: TEAM QUESTIONS

TEAM A

Q1: In which constellation would you find Sirius – the dog star?

Q2: Which pop group were the central feature of the 1980 film "Can't Stop the Music", which also starred Valerie Perrine?

Q3: Which of the Seven Wonders of the Ancient World was to be found at Halicarnassus in Asia Minor?

Q4: In Australian slang, what is a "dishlicker"?

Q5: Spell "Britannia" (as in Rule Britannia)

Q6: Which town is the administrative centre of the Northern Irish District of Fermanagh?

TEAM B

Q1: Which is the smallest and brightest constellation in the Southern Hemisphere night sky?

Q2: Which two actors were "The Blues Brothers" in the 1980 film of the same name?

Q3: Which of the Seven Wonders of the Ancient World was to be found at Rhodes, in the Aegean Sea?

A4: In aboriginal, and in Australian slang, what is a "jumbuck"?

Q5: Spell "Personnel" (as in Personnel Officer)

Q6: Which town in the administrative centre of the Northern Irish District of Down?

Q7: Which pop song by Elvis Costello begins: "There are some things you can't cover up with lipstick and powder; But I heard you mention my name, can't you talk any louder"?

Q8: Against which King of England did the barons' leader Simon de Montfort rebel?

Q7: Which pop song by Prince begins: "It's been seven hours and fifteen days since you took your love away; I go out every night and sleep all day since you took your love away"?

Q8: By what name was Sir Henry Percy (1364–1403) better known?

SPARE QUESTIONS
FOR USE IN CASE OF MISTAKE OR DISPUTE

Q: Whose Law of Finance, dating from the 19th century, can be described as "bad money drives out good money"?

Q: What is the most common cause of death in the South American country Columbia?

Q: On 2nd May, 1982, the British Government declared a how-many-mile exclusion zone around the Falkland Islands?

Q: Which New York workshop for professional actors was run by Lee Strasberg from 1949 to 1982?

NATIONAL MARTELL/RNLI QUIZ LEAGUE

MARTELL
COGNAC

SET OF QUESTIONS FOR MATCH NO. 8

ROUND ONE: TEAM QUESTIONS
A GENERAL KNOWLEDGE ROUND

TEAM A

Q1: Which calendar month's lucky gemstone is a Topaz?

Q2: What kind of animal is an Ibex?

Q3: Which of the world's regulatory organisations is the I.W.C.?

Q4: What colour is the diagonal cross on the national flag of Jamaica?

TEAM B

Q1: How many happy years make up a Ruby Anniversary?

Q2: By what modern name do we know the disease formerly called "consumption"?

Q3: Which is the world's heaviest species of snake?

Q4: What colour is the stripe at the bottom of the South African flag?

ROUND TWO: TEAM QUESTIONS
A CURRENT AFFAIRS ROUND

TEAM A

Q1: Which former Labour MP for Liverpool Broadgreen went to prison in 1991 for failing to pay his poll tax?

Q2: Which bizarre American rock star did Czechoslovakia appoint as its "Cultural Ambassador to the West" in 1991?

TEAM B

Q1: Which former MP for Coventry South East was suspended from the labour Party in 1991 because of his links with Militant?

Q2: What was John Cairncross exposed as, in September 1991?

Q3: Which musician's memoirs, published in 1991, were entitled "Always Playing"?

Q3: Top BBC man John Drummond bitterly criticised Nigel Kennedy's recording of Vivaldi's Four Seasons" during 1991. Who was Drummond at that time?

Q4: By what name is the former "National Council For Civil Liberties" now known?

Q4: By what name is the former "Marriage Guidance Council" now known?

ROUND THREE: INDIVIDUAL QUESTIONS

TEAM A

Q1: What is "Lotus 1–2–3"?

Q2: Of which Football Club was Eric Morcambe a director?

Q3: Who was the last Tudor Monarch to rule England?

Q4: On a domestic oven, what Gas Mark is equivalent to 200 degrees Celoius?"

TEAM B

Q1: Of which Football Club was Tommy Trinder a director?

Q2: What colour is a "Black Box" aboard an aircraft?

Q3: How many cards are there in each suit of a standard deck of playing cards?

Q4: Of what are "fuggles" and "goldings" popular varieties?

ROUND FOUR: TEAM QUESTIONS
A SPORTING ROUND

TEAM A

Q1: What sport do the Pittsburgh Penguins play?

Q2: Which long jumper's 23-year old world record was broken by Mike Powell in 1991?

Q3: Name one of the three racecourses owned by the Horserace Betting Levy Board?

Q4: Which motor racing manufacturer was Jim Clark most closely associated with?

TEAM B

Q1: At what sport was the British player Cassandra Jackman the World Junior Champion?

Q2: The highest scoring player in Welsh Rugby Union history retired from the International side in August 1991. Who is he?

Q3: How many times have Argentina won the FIFA World Cup Final?

Q4: In which sport does The Leander Club participate?

HALF TIME

ROUND FIVE: TEAM QUESTIONS
AN ENTERTAINMENT ROUND

TEAM A

Q1: Which TV comedy duo starred in "Plaza Patrol" as security officers in a shopping mall?

Q2: Only two individuals have ever had four Oscar nominations for one film. Name one of them.

Q3: Who was the first ever subject of the British TV version of the show "This Is Your Life"?

Q4: The 1960s pop group "Hedgehoppers Anonymous" were associated with which branch of the Armed Services?

TEAM B

Q1: What is the title of John Sullivan's TV comedy series about a diffident, divorced school teacher?

Q2: For which 1981 film did Warren Beatty receive four Oscar nominations for acting, directing, writing and producing?

Q3: In the TV series "Dixon of Dock Green", which character was Dixon's son-in-law"

Q4: The 1960s pop group "The Joystrings" were associated with which organisation?

ROUND SIX: TEAM QUESTIONS
A THOROUGHLY BRITISH ROUND

TEAM A

Q1: Near which British City is Shotts High Security Prison?

Q2: Which town is the administrative centre of the County of South Yorkshire?

Q3: Which South of England beauty area overtook Beachy Head as the nation's favourite suicide spot during 1990?

Q4: Which King of England first adopted the family name "Windsor"?

TEAM B

Q1: Which building houses the largest bell in London?

Q2: Which of the modern mainland Scottish regions has the smallest head of population?

Q3: Where in England was the world's longest seaside pier?

Q4: Which King of England first built a fortress on what is now the site of Windsor Castle?

ROUND SEVEN: THE SPECIALIST ROUND
TEAM QUESTIONS ON PADDY ASHDOWN

TEAM A

Q1: In which country was Paddy Ashdown born?

TEAM B

Q1: Where in the U.K. was Ashdown's father a pig farmer?

Q2: To where did Ashdown's family move, when their farming business closed in 1959?

Q3: "Paddy" is a nickname; can you provide one of Mr. Ashdown's three proper Christian names?

Q4: Where was Ashdown posted by the Foreign Office, from 1971 to 1976?

Q2: Which English public school did Paddy Ashdown attend?

Q3: What is the christian name of Mrs Ashdown, Paddy's wife?

Q4: In what year did Ashdown become leader of the Liberal Democrats?

NOTE: THE SPECIALIST SUBJECT IN THE NEXT MATCH WILL BE THE T.V. PUPPET SERIES "THUNDERBIRDS"

FINAL ROUND: TEAM QUESTIONS ON HEROES AND ANTI-HEROES

TEAM A

Q1: For what particular charitable work was Father Damian renowned in the nineteenth century?

Q2: Which wealthy hotel owner, imprisoned in 1992 for tax evasion, is alleged to have said "only the little people pay taxes"?

Q3: Who was Dwight D. Eisenhower's Vice President of the USA from 1953 to 1961?

Q4: Which 19th century statesman helped to abolish slavery, defended Carolyn of Brunswick in the House of Lords, and designed a horse-drawn carriage?

TEAM B

Q1: Who, in 1911, became unique in having won Nobel prizes in two different disciplines?

Q2: Which politician is the leader of the French National Front?

Q3: Which Tsar ruled Russia from 1547 to 1584?

Q4: By what more popular name was American political agitator El Haji Malik El Shabbazz better known?

END OF MAIN QUIZ

THE "GALLON" LEG: TEAM QUESTIONS

TEAM A

Q1: In arithmetic, how do you express as a decimal the fraction three fifths?

TEAM B

Q1: In arithmetic, what number is the square root of twenty five?

Q2: Name either of the two pubs destroyed by the I.R.A. in the 1975 Birmingham pub bombings.

Q3: What is the name of the ancestral home of the Duke of Bedford?

Q4: What is a "sand devil"?

Q5: The Irish writer Fingal O'Flaherty Wills was better known as whom?

Q6: In which country was Trotsky assassinated?

Q7: Who wrote the novel "Jamaica Inn"?

Q8: In which country is the port of Fray Bentos?

Q2: Which Brewer is based at the Unicorn Brewery, Stockport, Cheshire?

Q3: Who wrote the opera "The Barber of Seville"?

Q4: Where would you find an "assay mark"?

Q5: At what temperature Fahrenheit does water boil?

Q6: By what name is Gordon Sumner better known?

Q7: Who wrote the novel "The French Lieutenant's Woman"?

Q8: Which Asian country is bordered by China and the former USSR?

SPARE QUESTIONS
FOR USE IN CASE OF MISTAKE OR DISPUTE

Q: Who composed "Rhapsody in Blue"?

Q: What is the official residence of the Lord Mayor of London?

Q: What are "Billboard" and "Cashbox"?

Q: Linen is made from which plant?

SET OF QUESTIONS FOR MATCH NO. 9

ROUND ONE: TEAM QUESTIONS

TEAM A

Q1: Which snooker player regained the Womens' World Championship title in April 1993?

Q2: Which British off-shore island group contains the islands of Annet, Bryher and Samson?

Q3: Which rugby side were England playing, the day Erica Roe streaked at Twickenham?

Q4: Which BBC TV comedy series was filmed on location on Lister Avenue, Balby, Doncaster?

TEAM B

Q1: Which athlete won the Women's New York Marathon in November 1991, at her first attempt?

Q2: Which Archbishop of the Church of England is third in seniority after Canterbury and York?

Q3: Who, in October 1991, briefed John Major at 10 Downing Street about Gay Rights?

Q4: How many letters make up the Greek alphabet?

ROUND TWO: TEAM QUESTIONS

TEAM A

Q1: What colour is "Eau de Nil"?

Q2: Which two European countries made up the Dual Monarchy from 1867 until 1918?

Q3: In capital punishment terms, which is "Halifax Law"?

TEAM B

Q1: Jersey, Guernsey and Sark are three of the Channel Islands. Name the other two.

Q2: Which two European countries made up the Dual Alliance from 1893 until 1917?

Q3: What is a female aviator called?

Q4: Which of the planets of the solar system has sixteen satellites?

Q4: What title is given to the officer of the English peerage who presides over the College of Heralds?

ROUND THREE: INDIVIDUAL QUESTIONS

TEAM A

Q1: What is collected by a "discophile"?

Q2: How many are left when a baker's dozen is removed from a gross?

Q3: In Britain we call it "Sellotape", what do Australians call it?

Q4: In which English city would you find Aston University?

TEAM B

Q1: According to the Alliance & Leicester television advert, where do you find a "dafter invester"?

Q2: A heavy drinker of alcohol may well end up with DT's. What do the initials D.T. stand for?

Q3: In which English county would you find Hever Castle?

Q4: A pastry filled with dried fruit and a town in Greater Manchester share the same name. What is it?

ROUND FOUR: TEAM QUESTIONS

TEAM A

Q1: What was the profession of John Boyd Dunlop, who devised the first successful pneumatic tyre?

Q2: Who was the first male tennis player to win a Grand Slam of singles titles?

Q3: What does the word "Dermatoid" mean?

Q4: Which rock star's hit albums have included "My Aim is True", "Get Happy!" and "Spike"?

TEAM B

Q1: Who was the first woman tennis player to win a Grand Slam of singles titles?

Q2: Which London Teaching Hospital is situated immediately nearby The Old Bailey Law Courts?

Q3: Which popular British singer of the 1950s has been dubbed "the girl with the laugh in her voice"?

Q4: What kind of material is "lucite"?

HALF TIME

ROUND FIVE: TEAM QUESTIONS

TEAM A

Q1: How many vowels are there in the Greek alphabet?

Q2: Which town is the administrative centre of the County of East Sussex?

Q3: What is the name of the Maori dance performed by the All Blacks before a rugby match?

Q4: Who was the President of the Irish Republic from 1959 to 1973?

TEAM B

Q1: Which Irish poet is particularly associated with County Sligo?

Q2: Name one of the two planets in the solar system that only have two satellites.

Q3: The old East Riding of Yorkshire has been substantially swallowed up by which modern English county?

Q4: Which famous ship was discovered beneath a barrow by the River Deben, in East Anglia, in 1939?

ROUND SIX: TEAM QUESTIONS

TEAM A

Q1: Which golfer is the only one to have won a major tournament in the 1950s, the 1960s, the 1970s, and the 1980s?

Q2: Which current pop group are husband and wife combination Tracy Thorn and Ben Watts?

Q3: Which Brewer is based at The Archer Brewery, Salisbury, Wilts?

Q4: What is Zoisite?

TEAM B

Q1: With which sport would you associate William Harrison Dempsey?

Q2: Whose only No. 1 hit single in the U.K. was entitled "Where Are You Now, My Love"?

Q3: Which Brewer is located at Henley on Thames, Oxfordshire?

Q4: How or from what, is "Mother Of Pearl" obtained?

ROUND SEVEN: THE SPECIALIST ROUND
TEAM QUESTIONS ON THE TV PUPPET SERIES "THUNDERBIRDS"

TEAM A

Q1: Where is Tracy Island, the secret base of Thunderbirds, located?

Q2: Which of the Tracy boys is the one left up in space, all on his own?

TEAM B

Q1: What is the Tracy's secret organisation called?

Q2: What was the title of the Thunderbirds 1968 spin-off feature film?

Q3: What was the title of the Mermaid Theatre's long-running stage show based on Thunderbirds?

Q4: Which Thunderbird vehicle does Gordon Tracy pilot?

Q3: Who is the tyrannical villain with hypnotic powers who opposes International Rescue?

Q4: After what common theme were the five Tracy boys named?

NOTE: THE SPECIALIST SUBJECT IN THE NEXT MATCH WILL BE THE CITY OF OXFORD

FINAL ROUND: TEAM QUESTIONS

TEAM A

Q1: WHAT YEAR? National Service for British men ends; Harold Macmillan delivers his "Winds of Change" speech to the South African Parliament; Lonnie Donegan's "My Old Man's A Dustman" is a No. 1 hit.

Q2: Which actor portrayed the sound recordist at the centre of the 1981 film "Blow Out"?

Q3: Which semi-legendary medieval German scholar sold his soul in exchange for knowledge and power?

Q4: Which Independent Local Radio Station serves the Southampton and Portsmouth area?

TEAM B

Q1: WHAT YEAR? Pope John XXIII dies; Valentina Tereshkova becomes the first woman in space; Cliff Richard takes "Summer Holiday" to No. 1 in the pop charts.

Q2: Which Independent Local Radio Station serves the County of Kent?

Q3: Who was the Roman god of flowers, youth and Spring?

Q4: Which actor portrayed the photographer at the centre of the 1966 film "Blow Up"?

END OF MAIN QUIZ

THE "GALLON" LEG: TEAM QUESTIONS

TEAM A

Q1: What was the surname of Lady Jane Grey, after she married the Duke of Northumberland's son?

Q2: Which movie was the only ever "Sequel" to win a Best Picture Oscar?

TEAM B

Q1: In which pantomime does the character Widow Twankey appear?

Q2: London Underground's Gillespie Road Tube Station changed its name to accommodate which sporting club?

Q3: Who was England's Rugby Union coach during the 1991 World Cup competition?

Q4: Which charitable scientific society runs Regents Park Zoo?

Q5: The Cornish towns of Falmouth and St. Mawes stand at the mouth of which huge natural harbour?

Q6: What happened to the British Museum's "Portland Vase" in 1845?

Q7: The "Ebro" is the second largest river in which country?

Q8: Name either of the co-stars in William Wyler's 1953 film "Roman Holiday"

Q3: The most dangerous work in Britain kills one person every eight days. What job is involved?

Q4: Overboard which boat did tycoon Robert Maxwell lose his life?

Q5: Which English Island contains the towns of Queensborough, Minster and Leysdown on Sea?

Q6: Which Italian town was home to the Italian violin maker Antonio Stradivari?

Q7: What word describes the study of relationships between living organisms and their environments?

Q8: Who in 1896 wrote the first ever novel about cycling, entitled "The Wheels of Chance"?

SPARE QUESTIONS
FOR USE IN CASE OF MISTAKE OR DISPUTE

Q: Which performer's original version of the song "Instant Replay" was a Top 10 hit in 1978?

Q: To a craftsman, (apart from being a citizen of the Netherlands) what is a Dutchman?

Q: Ebbw Vale is in which Welsh county?

Q: With which sport do you associate Dawie de Villiers

SET OF QUESTIONS FOR MATCH NO. 10

ROUND ONE: TEAM QUESTIONS
ON A GEOGRAPHICAL SCALE

TEAM A

Q1: What is the name of the newly issued unit of currency in the independent Republic of Lithuania?

Q2: Cape Agulhas is the southernmost point of which continent?

Q3: On which Liverpool building will you find two famous Liver Birds?

Q4: Parts of which three old Counties were used in 1974 to create the West Midlands?

TEAM B

Q1: Which newly-independent Republic in the former Communist Bloc has issued a new unit of currency, the Kroon?

Q2: Which city is known as "The Venice of the North"?

Q3: What colour are the stars on the national flag of New Zealand?

Q4: After the Isle of Wight, which (in area) is the smallest modern English County?

ROUND TWO: TEAM QUESTIONS ON MUSIC

TEAM A

Q1: Which Englishman composed a symphonic study entitled "Falstaff"?

Q2: Which rock act took the song "Layla" into the Top ten in 1972 and 1982?

Q3: To which family of musical instruments does the saxophone belong?

Q4: By what stage name is gynaecologist Dr. Samm Hutt better known?

TEAM B

Q1: Which Italian composed the opera "Lucia Di Lammermoor"?

Q2: Which British rock 'n' roll singer's real name was Ronald Wycherley?

Q3: What musical value separates each fret on a guitar fingerboard?

Q4: Which rock band is the duo Per Gessle and Marie Fredriksson?

ROUND THREE: INDIVIDUAL QUESTIONS

TEAM A

Q1: Which book really was published during 1991 as a result of a Yellow Pages advertisement?

Q2: From which classic pop song does this line come?" "One of 16 vestal virgins who are leaving for the shore"?

Q3: In 1980, The Alexander Keilland tragedy killed 124 people. What was the "Alexander Keilland"?

Q4: How many children do the Prince and Princess of Wales have?

TEAM B

Q1: Which U.S. President ordered the boycott of the Moscow Olympic Games?

Q2: How many Pillars of Wisdom did Lawrence of Arabia write about?

Q3: From which classic pop song does this line come? "Well its one for the money, two for the show . . ."

Q4: On the shores of which Swiss lake does the town of Lucerne stand?

ROUND FOUR: TEAM QUESTIONS
A LITERARY ROUND

TEAM A

Q1: What kind of "Tattoo" did Tennesee Williams write about?

Q2: Which twentieth century poet wrote "Sweeny Erect" and "Sweeny Among the Nightingales"?

Q3: Which writer defended free speech by saying "I disapprove of what you say, but I defend to the death your right to say it"?

Q4: In another, earlier, novel the character Uncas is "The Last . . ." what?

TEAM B

Q1: Which classic children's fantasy adventure story is sub-titled "There and Back Again"?

Q2: "Burnt Norton", "East Coker" and "Little Gidding" are three parts of which T.S. Eliot work?

Q3: In F. Scott Fitzgerald's novel the character Monroe Stahr is "The Last . . ." what?

Q4: Which writer said, "A cynic is a man who knows the price of everything and the value of nothing"?

HALF TIME

ROUND FIVE: TEAM QUESTIONS
ON A MATTER OF HISTORY

TEAM A

Q1: WHAT YEAR? Ernest Saunders is sacked by the Board of Guinness plc; Zeebrugge Ferry disaster kills 180 people; "The Firm" are "Star Trekkin" at the top of the music charts.

Q2: Why were the Luddites so called?

Q3: What were introduced into the calendar in 1871, and were nicknamed "St. Lubbock's Days"?

Q4: What was Lenin's (Vladimir Ilyich Lenin, 1870–1924) original surname?

TEAM B

Q1: WHAT YEAR? The Tudor warship "Mary Rose" is raised; Channel Four TV opens; according to Fun Boy Three & Bananarama, "It Ain't What You Do, It's The Way That You Do It".

Q2: As what was Lucas van Leyden (1494–1535) famous?

Q3: In which city were the Luddites tried en mass in 1813, which resulted in many of them being hanged or transported?

Q4: What was the Russian city of St. Petersburg known as between 1914 and 1924?

ROUND SIX: TEAM QUESTIONS
ON RADIO AND TELEVISION

TEAM A

Q1: Which popular BBC Radio Four programme, presented by Jenni Murray, was given a controversial new time slot during 1991?

Q2: The character Paul Robinson on "Neighbours" is portrayed by which actor?

Q3: Which steeplejack was the subject of the series of TV films entitled "A Year With Fred"?

Q4: Which footballer's sister is an actress in the BBC Children's TV series "Byker Grove"?

TEAM B

Q1: Where on TV would you find "Miss Babs" and "Mrs Overall"?

Q2: Who is the compere of the TV game show "Wheel of Fortune"?

Q3: What was the title of Carla Lane's classic TV commedy series concerning a reluctant housewife and her dentist husband?

Q4: Which former "Doctor Who" played the Marsh-wiggle "Puddlegum" in the recent BBC dramatisation of "The Chronicles of Narnia"?

ROUND SEVEN: THE SPECIALIST ROUND
TEAM QUESTIONS ON THE CITY OF OXFORD

TEAM A

Q1: Who is the patron saint of the City of Oxford?

Q2: Which of the Oxford Colleges was founded by William of Wykeham, Bishop of Winchester, in 1379?

Q3: Which Oxford museum houses one of the world's great collections of ethnic art and anthropological culture?

Q4: Which river joins the Thames at Oxford?

TEAM B

Q1: Which was the first college to be founded at Oxford University?

Q2: Which Victorian poet dubbed Oxford "city of dreaming spires"?

Q3: Which world-famous marmalade manufacturer is located in Oxford?

Q4: Which district of Oxford, well known to Inspector Morse enthusiasts, lies between the University Press and the Oxford Canal?

NOTE: THE SPECIALIST SUBJECT IN THE NEXT MATCH WILL BE POP MUSIC – "SOUNDS OF THE SEVENTIES".

FINAL ROUND: TEAM QUESTIONS
A QUESTION OF SPORT

TEAM A

Q1: Which Rugby League side went 75 games without winning between October 1988 and March 1991?

Q2: In 1969, which country's cricket team bowled out the West Indies for 25 runs, and went on a remarkable 9 wicket victory?

Q3: Which official organisation controls horseracing in Britain?

Q4: Which "Latics" play football at Springfield Park

TEAM B

Q1: How many times have Italy won the Soccer World Cup

Q2: In the 1967 Grand National, which 100–1 horse won after a huge pile up at the twenty third fence?

Q3: Which Football League Club have Colin Addison, Tommy Docherty and Brian Clough all managed?

Q4: Cricket. Who was the captain of Somerset C.C.C. who sacked Viv Richards in 1986?

END OF MAIN QUIZ

THE "GALLON" LEG: TEAM QUESTIONS

TEAM A

Q1: Which character did Wayne Rogers play in the TV series M*A*S*H?

Q2: Spell "Intermediary"

Q3: In which year did Shakespeare die?

Q4: Phillipa Pearce wrote the classic children's book "Tom's . . ." what?

Q5: "Sr" is the chemical symbol for which element?

Q6: What motif is common to the cricket badges of Northamptonshire, Hampshire and Derbyshire?

Q7: How much money do you collect when you pass "Go" on an American Monopoly Board?

Q8: Which African country has recently changed its name to Burkina-Faso?

TEAM B

Q1: Which actor plays the part of Clegg in TV's "Last of the Summer Wine"?

Q2: Spell "Abysmal"

Q3: In which year did the Russians launch Sputnik I?

Q4: In Greek mythology, who was the Goddess of vengeance and retribution?

Q5: What number is represented by the Roman Numeral XM?

Q6: Who is the patron saint of actors and dancing?

Q7: Whose slogan used to be "Watch out, there's a Humphrey about"?

Q8: Baffin Bay lies between Baffin Island and which major land mass?

SPARE QUESTIONS
FOR USE IN CASE OF MISTAKE OR DISPUTE

Q: Which colour stripe is at the top to the German flag?

Q: In which prison was the dramatist Oscar Wilde incarcerated in the 1890's?

Q: What is Boy George's surname?

Q: In which area of Australia would you find the city of Darwin?

L7.10

SET OF QUESTIONS FOR MATCH NO. 11

ROUND ONE: TEAM QUESTIONS

TEAM A

Q1: What nationality is the wealthy financier Adnan Khashoggi?

Q2: In which British city was composer Frederick Delius born?

Q3: Which foodstuff do Americans call "Graham flour"?

Q4: If an Australian has "Kangaroos in the top paddock", what does it mean?

TEAM B

Q1: Who (in 1993) was Chairman of the BBC Board of Governors?

Q2: Who composed the musical score for the 1954 film "On the Waterfront"?

Q3: What kind of fish is an Arbroath Smokie?

Q4: To an Australian, what kind of foodstuffs is a "mystery bag"?

ROUND TWO: TEAM QUESTIONS

TEAM A

Q1: What kind of geographical feature is Ailsa Craig?

Q2: Which "Davis" retired from professional snooker in 1990?

Q3: Which contemporary female novelist wrote "The Good Terrorist" and "The Grass is Singing"?

TEAM B

Q1: Who discovered the Magnetic North Pole in 1831?

Q2: Which English football club were the first ever winners of the F.A. Premier League?

Q3: Which contemporary novelist wrote "The Raj Quartet", which included "The Jewel in the Crown"?

Q4: WHO'S THAT LADY? Born in London in 1902, this missionary led one hundred children out of China in 1940 to escape the Japanese; her story became famous.

Q4: WHO'S THAT LADY? She died of typhoid at Bergen Belsen Concentration Camp in 1945; but she is remembered (particularly by children) for her affirmation of life in the face of death and terror.

ROUND THREE: INDIVIDUAL QUESTIONS

TEAM A

Q1: Which of the signs of the Zodiac is "the Archer"?

Q2: Who was "The Sun King"?

Q3: According to the song, who was born on a mountain top in Tennessee?

Q4: Which famous land survey was compiled in 1086 on the orders of William The Conqueror?

TEAM B

Q1: Who is the host of the TV Quiz Show "Blockbusters"?

Q2: Which of the signs of the Zodiac is "the Balance"?

Q3: In the Rupert Bear stories, what is the name of the village where Rupert lives?

Q4: Why is your "funny bone" so called?

ROUND FOUR: TEAM QUESTIONS

TEAM A

Q1: In Shakespeare, who is it that suffers "The slings and arrows of outrageous fortune"?

Q2: Which Welsh mining story was filmed in 1941 by John Ford, and won an Oscar as the year's best picture?

Q3: What distinguishes a boat which is "clinker'built"?

Q4: Which cross-country British Rail route in England suffers the highest rate of train cancellations?

TEAM B

Q1: In 1941 which press baron refused to advertise or review the movie "Citizen Kane" in any of his papers?

Q2: In which English High Land Area will you find Mam Tor, "the shivering mountain"?

Q3: How many minutes late does a train have to be, before British Rail officially regard it as late?

Q4: In computer jargon, what does the acronym LISP stand for?

HALF TIME

TEAM A

Q1: Which English artillery officer devised deadly spherical case shot, first used against the Dutch in Surinam in 1803?

Q2: According to the "Acts of The Apostles" who was the first Christian Martyr?

Q3: After North Yorkshire, which is the second largest county in England?

Q4: What did the Northern Football Union, founded in 1895, become known as in 1922?

TEAM B

Q1: Which English furniture maker wrote in 1791 "The Cabinet Maker & Upholster's Drawing Book", and in 1802 "The Cabinet Dictionary"?

Q2: In the Christian calendar, which is St. Stephen's Day?

Q3: Which of the Isles of Scilly contains the communities of Old Grimsby and New Grimsby?

Q4: Which two nations participated in the first ever Rugby Union International Match (during the 1870-71 season)?

ROUND SIX: TEAM QUESTIONS

TEAM A

Q1: Which Island has Port Louis as its chief port and capital city?

Q2: In chess, how many Queens is a player theoretically able to use?

Q3: Which area of the UK is served by the Independent Radio Station "Downtown Radio"?

Q4: In the Old Testament, what was the name of the last King of Judah?

TEAM B

Q1: In a game of chess, which square is referred to by White as QR1?

Q2: Which Independent Local Radio Station is based in Glasgow?

Q3: In what place did God first appear to Moses?

Q4: In Shakespeare's "Merchant of Venice", which character falls in love with Bassanio?

ROUND SEVEN: THE SPECIALIST ROUND
TEAM QUESTIONS ON POP MUSIC – "SOUNDS OF THE SEVENTIES".

TEAM A

Q1: What was the first UK No 1 hit single of the 1970's?

TEAM B

Q1: Which controversial all-girl band had a hit LP called 'Cut", which Melody Maker called "the dirty, tousled, rag end of punk"?

Q2: Who had a Top Ten hit in 1974 with "Judy Teen"?

Q3: Whose mega dance hit in 1975 was "The Hustle"?

Q4: Which group's 1974 single "Queen of Clubs" was their first of many Top Ten hits?

Q2: Hot Gossip's first hit single named a featured artist – who?

Q3: Who had a No. 2 hit in 1970 with "Grooving With Mr. Bloe"?

Q4: Which was the last No. 1 hit single of the 1970's?

NOTE: THE SPECIALIST SUBJECT IN THE NEXT MATCH WILL BE IAN FLEMING'S JAMES BOND STORIES

FINAL ROUND: TEAM QUESTIONS

TEAM A

Q1: Who led the losing side at The Battle of Sedgemoor in 1685?

Q2: From which musical does the song "Till there was you" come?

Q3: Which brewer is based at the Wilderspool Brewery, in Warrington, Merseyside?

Q4: In astronomy, what does the word "magnitude" describe?

TEAM B

Q1: Which army won The Battle of Killiekrankie in 1689?

Q2: From which musical does the song "People" come?

Q3: Which brewer's beers are traditionally made at The Strangeways Brewery, Manchester?

Q4: Which is the brightest star in the night sky?

END OF MAIN QUIZ

THE "GALLON" LEG: TEAM QUESTIONS

TEAM A

Q1: Name the M.P. for Linlithgow whose revelations to Parliament exposed "The Belgrano Affair"?

Q2: Which Football League Club are nick-named "The Posh"

Q3: Which pop star recorded the following albums? "461 Ocean Boulevard"; "Slowhand"; "There's One in Every Crowd".

TEAM B

Q1: Which politician was known as the "Grand Old Man"

Q2: Who wrote the music score for the 1973 film "O Lucky Man"?

Q3: What is the principal monetary unit of Bulgaria?

Q4: What is the principal monetary unit of Austria?

Q4: Which day of the week is named after the Roman God of farming?

Q5: In the human body, which is the main olfactory oergan?

Q5: What was the name of Gene Autry's Horse?

Q6: The Colossus of Rhodes was a statue of whioh God?

Q6: The Hindu Trinity are Brahma, Shiva, and . . . whom?

Q7: In horror films and fiction, who is "Im-ho-tep"?

Q7: In comic books and films, what is Peter Parker's alter ego?

Q8: Which of Shakespeare's plays was banned from the stage during the period of King George III's insanity (1788–1820)?

Q8: Which of Lewis Carroll's characters taught Alice to dance the Lobster Quadrille?

SPARE QUESTIONS
FOR USE IN CASE OF MISTAKE OR DISPUTE

Q: What kind of sea-tide occurs at a new moon?

Q: The Egyptian God Anubis had the head of which animal?

Q: What is an assegai?

Q: Who sang the song "As Time Goes By" in the film "Casablanca"?

SET OF QUESTIONS FOR MATCH NO. 12

ROUND ONE: TEAM QUESTIONS

TEAM A

Q1: Which of the world's Republics (capital city Kishinev) was first annexed by Russia in 1812?

Q2: In which English County was composer Benjamin Brittan born?

Q3: Which rock band took its name from a classic Bing Crosby song?

Q4: Which sport are left-handed people banned from playing?

TEAM B

Q1: What was Moldavia known as prior to 1940?

Q2: In which English County was composer Ralph Vaughan Williams born?

Q3: Wich group originally recorded "Twist and Shout" in 1962?

Q4: With which sport was Sidney Wooderson associated?

ROUND TWO: TEAM QUESTIONS

TEAM A

Q1: "C" is the chemical symbol for which element?

Q2: In which English county would you find Lacock Abbey, the home of the Fox Talbot photographic museum?

Q3: What does the latin phrase "Mea Culpa" mean, in English?

Q4: What is the unit of weight used to measure silk, rayon or nylon yarn?

TEAM B

Q1: "Si" is the chemical symol for which element?

Q2: In which country would you find the "Titanic Cemetary"?

Q3: What does the latin phrase "In Vino Veritas" mean, in English?

Q4: In the USA, what does a "realtor" sell?

ROUND THREE: INDIVIDUAL QUESTIONS

TEAM A

Q1: Which famous stately home is situated at Woodstock, Oxfordshire?

Q2: Who is Canada's Head of State?

Q3: What name is given to a resident of the City of Southampton?

Q4: According to television advertising, who is the patron saint of pipe smokers?

TEAM B

Q: Prior to 1971, which letter of the alphabet represented one penny?

Q2: Who shot Billy the Kid?

Q3: In the Bible, who is the author of the Book of Revelation?

Q4: Which superheroine's alter ego is Diane Prince?

ROUND FOUR: TEAM QUESTIONS

TEAM A

Q: Which people did Odysseus meet on his travels, who drugged themselves to forget their own country?

Q2: Which Jewish French Army Officer was falsely imprisoned for treason in 1894, became a celebrated political cause, and was released in 1906?

Q3: The head of which animal, indigenous to North America, is featured on the badge of the Royal Canadian Mounted Police?

Q4: WHAT YEAR? Jayne Torvill and Christopher Dean win Olympic Gold; Miners go on strike; Ray Parker Junior's "Ghostbusters" is a hit in the music charts.

TEAM B

Q1: Which is the longest station platform on the British Rail network?

Q2: Which port in County Louth, north east Ireland, stands on the River Boyne and was the scene of the 1640 massacre by Cromwell of the inhabitants?

Q3: Which politician held the office of Canadian Prime Minister from 1921 to 1930 and from 1935 to 1948?

Q4: WHAT YEAR? Prince William, heir to the throne after Prince Charles, is born; Princess Grace of Monaco dies in a car crash; Irene Cara takes "Fame" into the pop charts.

HALF TIME

ROUND FIVE: TEAM QUESTIONS

TEAM A

Q1: In the Royal Navy he is called the "coxswain". What is he called in the Merchant Navy?

Q2: Which Football League Club has been managed since the War by Bob Stokoe, Bobby Moncur and Bill Shankly?

Q3: Where on a motor car would you find the "rack and pinion"?

Q4: Which poet wrote "The Dynasts" and "At the Railway Station, Upwey"?

TEAM B

Q1: "A Chair" is the collective name of what kind of craftsmen?

Q2: Which Football League Club has been managed by Ron Saunders, Joe Mercer and Tommy Docherty?

Q3: If distaff is the female side of a family, what name is given to the male side?

Q4: Which Victorian poet is remembered mainly for the poem "Say Not The Struggle Nought Availeth"?

ROUND SIX: TEAM QUESTIONS

TEAM A

Q1: Who shot Jesse James?

Q2: From which classic Bob Dylan song does this line come? – "I stumbled on the side of twelve misty mountains"

Q3: Which is Britain's largest "container port"?

Q4: In Norse mythology, who conducted the heroes who died in battle to Valhalla?

TEAM B

Q1: Who is the patron saint of gypsies?

Q2: From which classic rock and roll song does this line come? – "There's a car outside and it's all mine, just a '41 Ford, not a '59"

Q3: Name one of the two east coast States of the USA between which the Great Dismal Swamp is located.

Q4: In Norse mythology, whose personal attendants were the Valkyries?

ROUND SEVEN: THE SPECIALIST ROUND
TEAM QUESTIONS ON IAN FLEMING'S JAMES BOND STORIES

TEAM A

Q1: In which James Bond story was the CIA agent Felix Leiter first introduced?

Q2: What does the acronym SPECTRE stand for?

Q3: In which Bond story does 007 not even make an appearance until over half way through?

TEAM B

Q1: Which motor car was Bond associated with in the early stories?

Q2: In which story does 007 attempt to assassinate "M"?

Q3: At the end of which adventure does The Times publish 007's obituary?

Q4: In which story does Bond team up with Policewoman Gala Brand?

Q4: Smersh is a contraction of "Smiert Spionam", a secret department of Soviet Government. What does the phrase mean, in English?

NOTE: THE SPECIALIST SUBJECT IN THE NEXT MATCH WILL BE THE BATTLE OF WATERLOO, 1815

FINAL ROUND: TEAM QUESTIONS

TEAM A

Q1: In what sport would you adopt a "trudgen" style?

Q2: Which classical composer's music is most closely associated with Hovis bread, as a result of TV advertising?

Q3: Where in London is the new British Library buiding?

Q4: Which long-running BBC radio programme is presented by Clay Jones?

TEAM B

Q1: From which latin word is the Russian word "Tsar" a direct derivation?

Q2: Which classical composer's music is most closely associated with Old Spice after-shave, as a result of TV advertising?

Q3: In which London building is the old British Library Reading Room housed?

Q4: Which popular TV series of the 1970's was based on historical novels written by Winston Graham?

END OF MAIN QUIZ

THE "GALLON" LEG: TEAM QUESTIONS

TEAM A

Q1: In which city would you find the Italian stock exchange?

Q2: In cookery, what does the word "Julienne" mean?

Q3: Whose army destroyed Corfe Castle, in Dorset?

Q4: What is the main difference between a monkey and an ape?

Q5: What is the capital of Fiji?

TEAM B

Q1: In which city would you find the German stock exchange?

Q2: What is the name of the female character in Dickens' novel "Barnaby Rudge", after whom a hat was named?

Q3: Who was the most prolific hymn writer in history?

Q4: In which year was the 20 mph speed limit abolished in Britain?

Q5: Who currently holds the title "Duke of Normandy"?

Q6: Which health organisation is the W.C.R.F.?

Q7: Who directed the films "The African Queen" and "The Maltese Falcon"?

Q8: In which sport do "The Middlesbrough Bears" participate?

Q6: Which health organisation is the B.H.F.?

Q7: Which character was portrayed by Honour Blackman in the TV series "The Avengers"?

Q8: Which soccer club from north east England started life as "The Teachers"?

SPARE QUESTIONS
FOR USE IN CASE OF MISTAKE OR DISPUTE

Q: On a Monopoly Board, which property makes up the red set, along with The Strand and Trafalgar Square?

Q: With which English cricket county has Pakistani all-rounder Imran Khan been associated for the last decade?

Q: Who was sacked as the manager of Altrincham Town Football Club in 1988?

Q: Who wrote "The Exorcist"?

SET OF QUESTIONS FOR MATCH NO. 13

ROUND ONE: TEAM QUESTIONS
ROUND BRITAIN QUIZ

TEAM A

Q1: The River Wear runs through which two University cities?

Q2: At which London Mainline Station would you catch a train to Cambridge?

Q3: Of which off-shore island group is Mull a constituent part?

Q4: What was it that Thomas Hardy called "the Gibraltar of Wessex"?

TEAM B

Q1: Which is the county town of Northumberland?

Q2: In London, which hill overlooks Regents Park from the north?

Q3: Which town is the capital of the Isle of Mull?

Q4: On which Dorset heath would you find the Agglestone, weighing 500 tons?

ROUND TWO: TEAM QUESTIONS
ON WORDS AND PHRASES

TEAM A

Q1: Spell "rhythm" (the measured flow of music)

Q2: In Ireland, what is a "gombeen man"?

Q3: What does the latin phrase "in camera" mean, in English?

Q4: How does an animal become a "Pollard"?

TEAM B

Q1: Spell "catarrh" (an inflamation of the mucous membrane)

Q2: In France, what is a "framboise"? (pronounced frahn-bwarze)

Q3: Which latin phrase does the common abbreviation i.e. represent?

Q4: What is the heraldic term for a swastika?

ROUND THREE: INDIVIDUAL QUESTIONS

TEAM A

Q1: What is the principal monetary unit of Sri Lanka?

Q2: Between which two countries does The Aegian Sea lie?

Q3: What is a "polder"?

Q4: Who led the defence of Mafeking during the 2nd Anglo-Boer War?

TEAM B

Q1: What is chemotherapy?

Q2: On which television series was Landburger Gessler the villain?

Q3: How many time zones is the Earth divided into?

Q4: What is Sinophobia?

ROUND FOUR: TEAM QUESTIONS
FACE THE MUSIC

TEAM A

Q1: In the world of pop music, who are Andy Bell and Vince Clarke?

Q2: Which French comoser's operatic masterpiece was "Pelleas et Melisande"?

Q3: Which was the only member of The Beatles to play on the album track "Within You, Without You"?

Q4: Which piece of classical music did Cadbury's use to promote their "Fruit and Nut" chocolate?

TEAM B

Q1: From which country do the pop group "The Sugarcubes" hail?

Q2: Which American composer wrote the ballet "Appalachan Spring" in 1944?

Q3: Which track on The Beatles' "Rubber Soul" album was subtitled "This Bird Has Flown"?

Q4: Which piece of classical music did the Government use in their "H²Owner" Privatisation adverts?

HALF TIME

ROUND FIVE: TEAM QUESTIONS
ON PROVERBS AND QUOTATIONS

TEAM A

Q1: According to the proverb, what do big fleas have on their backs?

Q2: Which writer called Nell Gwynne "pretty witty Nell"?

Q3: According to the proverb, which animal always returns to its vomit?

TEAM B

Q1: According to the proverb, what is it that pays all debts?

Q2: Which poet wrote of the "still sad music of humanity"?

Q3: According to the proverb, what is a cat in gloves unable to do?

L7.14

Q4: Who, in 1991, accused Margaret Thatcher of not understanding Europe because she had a "minute brain"?

Q4: Which Daily Mirror journalist said of Robert Maxwell after his death, "He enriched my life. He was my inspiration and my hero"?

ROUND SIX: TEAM QUESTIONS
A QUESTION OF SPORT

TEAM A

Q1: Which team won the Formula One Motor Racing Constructors' Championship in 1988 and 1989?

Q2: Who was the New Zealand wicket keeper during the Kiwis' 1990 Test Cricket Series in England?

Q3: Which Spennymoor soccer referee officiated at the 1990 World Cup Finals?

Q4: In squash raquets, what is "a boast"?

TEAM B

Q1: Who took over the captaincy of Somerset Cricket Club in 1989?

Q2: What was broken at Iffley Road Oxford on May 6th 1954?

Q3: Which footballer captained Sunderland to their 1973 FA Cup Final victory?

Q4: In squash raquets, what is "a nick"?

ROUND SEVEN: THE SPECIALIST ROUND
TEAM QUESTIONS ON THE BATTLE OF WATERLOO, 1815

TEAM A

Q1: On what day and month was the Battle of Waterloo fought?

Q2: What crop was being grown on the farmland that was used as the battleground in 1815?

Q3: What classic defensive stragegy did Wellington's infantry adopt when attacked by 6000 French cavalry?

Q4: Who was Napoleon's second-in-command?

TEAM B

Q1: Where did Blücher tackle Napoleon's force on the 16th June, two days before the Battle of Waterloo?

Q2: Who commanded Wellington's cavalry (and lost his leg in the process) at Waterloo?

Q3: What was the name of the Inn outside which Wellington and Blücher met on the evening of the battle?

Q4: What major feature is prominent on the battlefield site now, but wasn't there in 1815?

NOTE: THE SPECIALIST SUBJECT IN THE NEXT MATCH WILL BE THE FORD CORTINA

FINAL ROUND: TEAM QUESTIONS
A MATTER OF POLITICS

TEAM A

Q1: Of which country was General Meza the Dictator, before fleeing to Argentina in 1981?

Q2: Which politician, sacked during 1992, claimed that one in every four Englishman was a homosexual?

Q3: Who was Lyndon B. Johnson's Vice-President of the USA from 1963 to 1969?

Q4: Which master spy's family was allowed to join him in Britain in September 1991?

TEAM B

Q1: Of which country was Colonel Mengistu the Dictator, before fleeing to Zimbabwe in 1991?

Q2: What were Pat Pottle and Michael Randle tried for, in 1991?

Q3: Who was Gerald Ford's Vice-President of the USA from 1974 to 1977?

Q4: How did Stuart Hughes of East Devon make history in the May 1991 Local Council Elections?

END OF MAIN QUIZ

THE "GALLON" LEG: TEAM QUESTIONS

TEAM A

Q1: In mathematics, what describes the ratio of a circle's circumference to its diameter?

Q2: In the comic "Viz", what is the name of the faithful Border Bin Liner?

Q3: In military terms, what is the D.L.I.?

Q4: Where was King James IV of Scotland defeated by the English in 1513?

Q5: Name the stretch of water that lies between China and Japan?

Q6: Who was the lead singer with the 1980s pop group "Teardrop Explodes"?

TEAM B

Q1: What, in the human eye, is the point called where vision is most acute?

Q2: In the comic "Viz", which character wears "Amazing Underpants"?

Q3: Who wrote, in 1949, the satirical novel "Love in a Cold Climate"?

Q4: Which English monarch was, in 1541, the first to assume the title of "King of Ireland"?

Q5: What is the capital city of Papua New Guinea?

Q6: Name both the actresses who starred in the 1970s TV series "Man About The House"?

Q7: On which English motorway would you find Watford Gap Services?

Q7: Who wrote "The Man in the Iron Mask"?

Q8: What is the capital city of Ethiopia?

Q8: Which city in the U.K. is known as the "Granite City"?

SPARE QUESTIONS
FOR USE IN CASE OF MISTAKE OR DISPUTE

Q: Pneumonia is inflammation of the lungs. Spell "pneumonia"

Q: What nationality is Perez de Cuellar, the former Secretary General of the United Nations?

Q: In musical notation, how many lines are there on a stave?

Q: Why was Causey Arch a significant structure in the history of railways?

SET OF QUESTIONS FOR MATCH NO. 14

ROUND ONE: TEAM QUESTIONS

TEAM A

Q1: Which classic movie features the adventures of Dorothy Gale?

Q2: What is "nacre" another term for?

Q3: Which celebrated modern novel celebrates the actuality of one day in Dublin on 16th June 1904?

Q4: Spell "adolescence"

TEAM B

Q1: What breed of dog was Crufts Supreme Champion in 1992?

Q2: George Bernard Shaw's character "Major Barbara" is a Major in which organisation?

Q3: Which Greek god of wealth is also an astronomical body discovered in 1930, and a cartoon character?

Q4: Spell "oestrogen" (pronounced eest-ro-genn)

ROUND TWO: TEAM QUESTIONS

TEAM A

Q1: Which major London railway terminus is situated in London SW1 (South West One)?

Q2: Born Marie Jeanne Becu (circa 1743), she became the mistress of Louis the Fifteenth and died in 1793 on the guillotine. Who was she?

Q3: What does the phrase "Janus-faced" mean?

Q4: How many red stripes appear on the national flag of the United States of America?

TEAM B

Q1: Which famous London thoroughfare runs from Buckingham Palace along the south side of St. James Park?

Q2: Who was the second King of the Hebrews (about 1000–962 BC) that united Israel and made Jerusalem its capital?

Q3: What part of the human body is the "ulna nerve"?

Q4: Which is the biggest structure in the world built by living creatures?

ROUND THREE: INDIVIDUAL QUESTIONS

TEAM A

Q1: What are the territorial divisions of Switzerland called?

Q2: What is an "oast house"?

Q3: Who compiled the first English Dictionary?

Q4: Who was the first woman to fly from Britain to Australia?

TEAM B

Q1: What is a "tonsure"?

Q2: How many legs has a fly got?

Q3: What is the former name of Istanbul?

Q4: How many years make up a bi-centenary?

ROUND FOUR: TEAM QUESTIONS

TEAM A

Q1: Which football club returned to the Football League for the 1990–91 season?

Q2: What is the name of the channel which lies between South East Greenland and Iceland?

Q3: If food is served "en croute" what would it be like?

Q4: Which British Cabinet Minister discovered he had a sex therapist living in the basement of his house, during 1991?

TEAM B

Q1: In 1971, the footballer Colin Todd left Sunderland to join which League club?

Q2: Into which body of water do the rivers Ural and Volga both drain?

Q3: From which game does the phrase "all at sixes and sevens" originate?

Q4: Which basketball player retired in 1991 because he was confirmed HIV positive?

HALF TIME

ROUND FIVE: TEAM QUESTIONS

TEAM A

Q1: WHAT YEAR? John Hinckley shoots President Reagan; Bobby Sands goes on hunger strike; Cliff Richard is "Wired for Sound".

Q2: By what name was Sister Luc Gabrielle more popularly known?

TEAM B

Q1 WHAT YEAR? W.P.C. Yvonne Fletcher is killed by a Libyan diplomat; York Minster goes up in flames; Liverpool win the European Champions Cup.

Q2: What nationality was The Singing Nun?

Q3: Which is the earliest surviving example of a naval vessel mounting guns broadside within its hull?

Q4: Which Victorian poet wrote "Empedocles on Etna" and "Dover Beach"?

Q3: When "The Mallard" set its world speed record for a steam locomotive in 1938, what speed did it attain?

Q4: Which Victorian poet wrote "Ring and Book" and "Paracelsus"?

ROUND SIX: TEAM QUESTIONS

TEAM A

Q1: In TV science-fiction, whose ship was "The Liberator"?

Q2: Who fired the gun which caused Derek Bentley to be hanged in 1953?

Q3: Which cricket county won the 1991 Nat West Trophy Final?

Q4: One of Ireland's primary ferry ports has a name which is pronounced "Dunn Leery'. How is the name actually spelled?

TEAM B

Q1: In "Star Trek: the Next Generation" which actress portrays the hostess Guinan?

Q2: Where in Peking is the Mausoleum of Mao Tse-tung (where his embalmed body is on display) to be found?

Q3: What originally ran from Hambledon Lock to Henley Bridge?

Q4: One of the colleges of Oxford University has a name which is pronounced "Maudlin". How is the name actually spelled?

ROUND SEVEN: THE SPECIALIST ROUND
TEAM QUESTIONS ON THE FORD CORTINA

TEAM A

Q1: In which year was the first Mark I Cortina produced?

Q2: Between 1962 and 1964 what word was featured on the Mark I Cortina's bonnet badge?

Q3: What was the exterior colour scheme of the original Lotus Cortinas?

Q4: Which American Ford Model's engine was used to power the Mark III and Mark IV Cortinas?

TEAM B

Q1: What happened in 1960 which provided the inspiration for the car being called "The Cortina"?

Q2: What was the engine size (capacity) of the original Cortina model?

Q3: In what year was the Mark IV Cortina launched?

Q4: In May 1982, the last of the Cortinas were marketed under what special name?

NOTE: THE SPECIALIST SUBJECT IN THE NEXT MATCH WILL BE "THE MARINES, 1664–1815".

FINAL ROUND: TEAM QUESTIONS

TEAM A

Q1: Football. How many times were Liverpool F.C. League Champions during the 1950s and 1960s?

Q2: Which Northern Irish county is known as "The Lake District of Northern Ireland"?

Q3: What is an "interregnum"?

Q4: Of which war-time deception story was the fictitious Captain William Martin of the Royal Marines the dead hero?

TEAM B

Q1: Which Football Club were Scottish League Champions in 1980, 1984 and 1985?

Q2: With which 1930's social protest would you particularly associate the name of Ellen Wilkinson?

Q3: What does the prefix "infra" mean?

Q4: Which fictitious country developed superpower ambitions and a space programme in the classic British films "The Mouse That Roared" and "Mouse on the Moon"?

END OF MAIN QUIZ

THE "GALLON" LEG: TEAM QUESTIONS

TEAM A

Q1: In the Bible, who sold his birthright for a mess of potage?

Q2: What is a "lepidopterist"?

Q3: From what substance is turpentine obtained?

Q4: Which American rock 'n' roll singer died in England, in a car crash, in 1960?

Q5: Where on your body would a "witlow" form?

Q6: Who created the fictional detective Father Brown?

Q7: Where in the USA is Arlington Cemetary?

Q8: In which English city were the Protestant martyrs – Latimer, Ridley and Cranmer – burnt at the stake?

TEAM B

Q1: What was the name of Esau's brother?

Q2: What is a "howdah"?

Q3: From what substance is laudanum obtained?

Q4: Name either of the other two rock 'n' roll singers who died with Buddy Holly in the 1959 plane crash?

Q5: Where in the human body is the pituitary gland located?

Q6: Who created the fictional character Peter Pan?

Q7: Where is the Alhambra Palace?

Q8: Who was the real life "Little Bo Peep", about whom the nursery rhyme was coined?

Q: Which New York daily newspaper did Robert Maxwell own, at the time of his death?

Q: Where on a motor car, would you find the "needle valve"?

Q: Which historic ship functions as an art gallery on the Thames Embankment, near Hungerford Bridge?

Q: What phrase was the subject of a Biblical dream, is a plant and a way of boarding a ship?

L7.16

SET OF QUESTIONS FOR MATCH NO. 15

ROUND ONE: TEAM QUESTIONS

TEAM A

Q1: Which sports commentator spoke the classic words "They think it's all over. It is now!"

Q2: Which Independent Local Radio Station is based in Peterborough and serves the Fens?

Q3: What is the official name of the highest court of civil jurisdiction in Scotland?

Q4: Whose orchestra had a Top Ten Hit in 1960 with "Theme from A Hidden Place"?

TEAM B

Q1: In which sport can you adopt "catch as catch can" rules?

Q2: Which Independent Local Radio Station is based in Norwich, and serves the County of Norfolk?

Q3: Whose orchestra had a hit record in 1961 with the song "Sucu Sucu"? (You have a choice of three)

Q4: What is a "craniometer"?

ROUND TWO: TEAM QUESTIONS

TEAM A

Q1: In which U.S. State is the city of Chatanooga to be found?

Q2: What name is shared by an assistant to a parish priest, and a long-stemmed clay tobacco pipe?

Q3: Which actor portrays Victor Meldrew in the T.V. sit-com "One Foot in the Grave?"

Q4: At which Race Course is the King George the Sixth and Queen Elizabeth Diamond Stakes run?

TEAM B

Q1: In which U.S. State is the city of Santa Fe to be found?

Q2: In which T.V. situation comedy do Victor and Margaret Meldrew face up to the problems of retirement?

Q3: Which Gloucestershire town did the Romans call "Corinium"?

Q4: Which British Motor Racing driver died in July 1991, when his Formula 3000 car burst into flames?

ROUND THREE: INDIVIDUAL QUESTIONS

TEAM A

Q1: Which Ancient King overthrew the Jewish monarchy, and led the Jews to captivity in Babylon?

Q2: Who is the Archbishop of Westminster?

Q3: In English, what does the phrase "Ave Maria" mean?

Q4: Which two metals were traditionally combined to make pewter?

TEAM B

Q1: In English, what does the phrase "bona fide" mean?

Q2: Which famous son inherited the conquests of his father Philip of Macedon in the 4th century B.C.?

Q3: Which two world leaders drew up the 1941 "Atlantic Treaty"?

Q4: Which award for seaplane racing was organised by the Aero Club de France in the early part of this century?

ROUND FOUR: TEAM QUESTIONS

TEAM A

Q1: When is the Earth at its "aphelion"?

Q2: Which children's T.V. programme was presented by Ross King and Charlotte Hindle?

Q3: Which Romantic Englishman, who died in 1824, was known as "the Boxing Poet"?

Q4: Every year in the British Open Championship a golfer will win the prestigious "Silver Medal". What for?

TEAM B

Q1: When is the Moon at its "apogee"?

Q2: Who presented the T.V. amateur talent show "Stars in Their Eyes"?

Q3: At which golf course was the 1993 British Open Golf Championship held?

Q4: What is Japanese "Haiku"? (pronounced Hi – koo)?

HALF TIME

ROUND FIVE: TEAM QUESTIONS

TEAM A

Q1: In which classic film was the character Dr. Alec Harvey frustrated in his attempts to have an affair?

TEAM B

Q1: The old Welsh County of Cardigan has been absorbed into which modern County?

Q2: Which town is the administrative capital of Dyfed?

Q3: What do the initials G.C.H.Q. stand for?

Q4: From which Football League Club did Manchester United sign Gary Pallister for £2.3 million, in 1989?

Q2: Which composer's music was used on the soundtrack of the film "Brief Encounter"?

Q3: In computer jargon, what does "Fortran" stand for?

Q4: Which Football Club sold Ian Rush to Liverpool F.C. for £2.8 million in 1988?

ROUND SIX: TEAM QUESTIONS

TEAM A

Q1: In which country is the language Fanti spoken?

Q2: Spell "caterwaul"

Q3: Which singer had a No. 1 hit
• record in 1984 with "Careless Whisper"?

Q4: For which English Cricket County was Ian Greig the captain?

TEAM B

Q1: In which modern country is Mount Ararat?

Q2: Spell "ephemeral"

Q3: Which singer had a No. 1 hit single in 1977 with "Way Down"?

Q4: For which English Cricket County is Kim Barnett the captain?

ROUND SEVEN: THE SPECIALIST ROUND
TEAM QUESTIONS ON THE MARINES, 1664–1815

TEAM A

Q1: The Marines were known as "The Duke of York and Albany's Maritime Regiment of Foot" when raised on 28th October 1664. By what other title were they known?

Q2: The Marines captured and held under an intensive siege the Rock of Gibraltar in what year?

Q3: What was the name of the woman who served as a Marine (undetected) from 1745 to 1750?

Q4: Which battle in 1761 is celebrated every year to this day on 7th June?

TEAM B

Q1: When the "Corps of Marines" were formed in 1755, they were stationed at three principal dockyard ports. Name them.

Q2: When inspecting a Marine guard of honour aboard HMS Bellerophon in July 1815, he remarked "Much might be done by a hundred thousand soldiers such as these". Who said these words?

Q3: Major Pitcairn commanded the Marines at which famous battle on 17th June 1775?

Q4: At Belle Isle, the French gave a particular nickname to the Marines. What was it?

FINAL ROUND: TEAM QUESTIONS

TEAM A

Q1: In Greek mythology, who killed Medusa, the mortal Gorgon?

Q2: In Binary mathematics, what number is represented by the notation "10" (one zero)?

Q3: What sport do the Pittsburg Pirates play?

Q4: What was the name of the Church established by the followers of the mystic Emmanuel Swedenborg?

TEAM B

Q1: In Greek mythology, what was the name of Priam's daughter, to whom Apollo gave the gift of prophecy?

Q2: In Binary mathematics, what number is represented by the notation "100" (one zero zero)?

Q3: Which League football team is nicknamed "The Railwaymen"?

Q4: Who was the last British monarch to refuse the Royal Assent to an Act of Parliament?

END OF MAIN QUIZ

THE "GALLON" LEG: TEAM QUESTIONS

TEAM A

Q1: Who was appointed Prime Minister of France in May 1990?

Q2: What is the Jewish "Talmud"?

Q3: What social phenomenon occurred on American Max Yasgur's farm, in August 1969?

Q4: In which country does "The School of the Air", a form of radio education, operate?

Q5: Name either of the two rivers between which the Kalahari Desert lies.

TEAM B

Q1: In which European country is the city of Sienna?

Q2: B.C.C.I. was closed by The Bank of England in July 1991. What do the initials B.C.C.I. stand for?

Q3: Where in London is the Science Museum?

Q4: Which word means "the ability to read and write in one's own language"?

Q5: During which Wars did Julius Caesar launch his two unsuccessful invasions of Britain?

Q6: Which Scottish Region is bordered by Strathclyde, Tayside and Grampian?

Q7: Name either of the other two ingredients that cocaine is blended with to make "Crack"

Q8: What monetary value was a pre-decimal crown?

Q6: Which English city was known to the Anglo Saxons as "Gipeswic"? (Pronounced gippers-wick)

Q7: What monetary value was the pre-decimal florin?

Q8: What part of the human body is affected by Bright's Disease?

SPARE QUESTIONS
FOR USE IN CASE OF MISTAKE OR DISPUTE

Q: The Imperial War Museum stands on the site of which notorious hospital?

Q: Which high level trunk road links Penrith with Scotch Corner, and is commonly closed by snow in winter?

Q: In which Canadian territory is the Klondyke?

Q: Who wrote the novel "A Room With A View"?

SET OF QUESTIONS FOR MATCH NO. 16

ROUND ONE: TEAM QUESTIONS

TEAM A

Q1: Which notorious debtor's prison stood on the east side of London's Farringdon Street until its demolition in 1846?

Q2: Who was the last British King to be crowned in Scotland?

Q3: Which snooker player carried the Olympic Torch part of the way to Melbourne in 1956?

Q4: WHO'S THAT LADY? Born 1910 in Czechoslovakia, she became a respected anthropological and wildlife authority in Africa. She was murdered in grisly circumstances in 1980.

TEAM B

Q1: Which pioneering British physician was the country's first female Mayor?

Q2: In a Scottish court of law, the jury can find the accused "guilty", "not guilty", or . . . what?

Q3: Which American Football star appeared in the film "Towering Inferno"?

Q4: WHO'S THAT LADY? A singer, born in Texas in 1943, she was a hard living, hard-drinking performer. She died of a heroine overdose in 1970.

ROUND TWO: TEAM QUESTIONS

TEAM A

Q1: Which Scottish International was 1991 Footballer of the Year in the English League?

Q2: Which publication begins with the words "The history of all hitherto existing society is the history of class struggles"?

TEAM B

Q1: Which English Football League Club were 2nd Division Champions in 1990–91?

Q2: In which language was the Communist Manifesto first published, in 1848?

Q3: Angora, where the cats come from, is the old name for which modern city?

Q3: Who wrote the 19th century minstrel songs "Oh Susanna!" and "Beautiful Dreamer"?

Q4: In which James Bond story is Emilio Largo the villain?

Q4: Which villain did James Bond find on "Crab Key"?

ROUND THREE: INDIVIDUAL QUESTIONS

TEAM A

Q1: Species of which mammal can be Grey, Blue, Right or Pilot?

Q2: Which is the last bridge over the Thames, before the sea?

Q3: Whose best-selling book about the lives of the rich is called "Polo"?

Q4: Who was Michael Farraday?

TEAM B

Q1: Which is the indigenous religion of Japan?

Q2: Where in New York are the U.S. Open Tennis Championships held?

Q3: Whose portrait appears on the reverse of the current Bank of England Twenty Pound note?

Q4: Which body of water was governed by The Hanseatic League in the 15th and 16th centuries?

ROUND FOUR: TEAM QUESTIONS

TEAM A

Q1: Two of South America's nations are land-locked. Name one of them.

Q2: What is mixed with milk or water to make gruel?

Q3: Which legendary warlord united the Irish against Viking control in 1002 AD?

Q4: Railways. Which Preserved Line runs from Wooton to Havenstreet?

TEAM B

Q1: In which real life country is there an area called "Never Never Land"?

Q3: Which profession supposedly works on "Grub Street"?

Q3: Which King of England was authorised by Pope Adrian IV (the only English Pope) to subjugate Ireland for the Roman Catholic Church?

Q4: Which Preserved Steam Railway Line links Sheffield Park to Horsted Keynes?

HALF TIME

ROUND FIVE: TEAM QUESTIONS

TEAM A

Q1: Which was Vince Hill's only Top Ten hit single in the U.K.?

Q2: In which body of water do the Netherlands Antilles lie?

Q3: Which 1980's pop group used to be fronted by singer Feargal Sharkey?

Q4: Which was the last of the Confederate States to surrender in the American Civil War?

TEAM B

Q1: By what name was TV comic Richard Hearne better known in the 1950s?

Q2: Which is the only one of the world's continents where you wouldn't find Barn Owls?

Q3: Which rank in the British Army is signified by a single crown?

Q4: Which English League Football Club are nicknamed "The Hornets"?

ROUND SIX: TEAM QUESTIONS

TEAM A

Q1: Name the stretch of water that lies between Finland and Sweden.

Q2: Which children's author created "The Borrowers"?

Q3: Which is the ninth of the Ten Commandments?

Q4: Which country's monetary unit is the Markka?

TEAM B

Q1: Reg Dwight and Pauline Matthews reached No. 1 in the pop charts in 1976. With what record?

Q2: In which country's sector of the North Sea is the Ekofisk oil field?

Q3: "Concorde" is the capital of which U.S. State?

Q4: On which London Underground line lies Heathrow Airport?

ROUND SEVEN: THE SPECIALIST ROUND
TEAM QUESTIONS ON YUGOSLAVIA – BEFORE THE BREAK UP

TEAM A

Q1: Yugoslavia was a federation of six republics, Serbia, Croatia & Slovenia were three of them. Name two others.

Q2: Which city is the capital of Serbia?

Q3: What racial group is predominent in Serbia's troublesome Kosovo region?

TEAM B

Q1: Which three colours made up the stripes on the Yugoslavian flag?

Q2: Which city is the capital of Macedonia?

Q3: What was the name of the Serbian pro-Royalist guerilla group during World War Two?

Q4: Which was the last King of Yugoslavia, who went into exile in 1941?

Q4: Which Dalmatian port is known to the Italians as "Ragusa"?

FINAL ROUND: TEAM QUESTIONS

TEAM A

Q1: Who was Wimbledon Men's singles Champion in 1991?

Q2: Which of Ernest Hemingway's stories, filmed with Rock Hudson in 1957, features Frederic Henry, an American ambulance driver during World War One?

Q3: Where in England is an acre of land given to the U.S.A. in memory of John F. Kennedy?

Q4: What foodstuff can be "Navy" "Garbano" or "Aduki"?

TEAM B

Q1: Who was Britain's only individual gold medal winner at the 1991 World Athletics Championships in Tokyo?

Q2: Who wrote the classic TV comedy serious, "The Fall and Rise of Reginald Perrin"?

Q3: Which range of mountains lies immediately to the east of Aviemore in the Scottish Highlands?

Q4: If you are allergic to wheat, what sort of diet must you go onto?

END OF MAIN QUIZ

THE "GALLON" LEG: TEAM QUESTIONS

TEAM A

Q1: Which motorway links London and Canterbury?

Q2: What is an "Abernethy"?

Q3: Which King of England is buried at Caen, in France?

Q4: How many books are there in The New Testament?

Q5: Who wrote "The Vicar of Wakefield"?

Q6: In Greek mythology, what was the name of the winged horse?

TEAM B

Q1: Which motorway links the cities of Glasgow and Edinburgh?

Q2: Which common British bird has the latin name "Pica Pica"?

Q3: Which French vegetable dish is made of tomatoes, aubergines, onions and sweet peppers cooked in olive oil?

Q4: Which is the last book in The Bible?

Q5: Who wrote "Swallows and Amazons"?

Q6: Which punk rock group was fronted by singer Annabelle Lewin?

Q7: What is the name of the Parliament of the Irish Republic?

Q8: Which was the first of the James Bond novels to be published?

Q7: Which Shakespeare character was dubbed "the noblest Roman of them all"

Q8: In Greek mythology, who was the mother of Achilles?

SPARE QUESTIONS
FOR USE IN CASE OF MISTAKE OR DISPUTE

Q: Who was British Prime Minister when the first stretch of British motorway was opened?

Q: Which film did The Beatles make in 1965?

Q: Who, in Irish public life, is the Taoiseach? (pronounced Tee-shock)

Q: What is the principal monetary unit of Syria?

NATIONAL MARTELL/RNLI QUIZ LEAGUE

MARTELL COGNAC

QUIZ ANSWERS

SET OF ANSWERS FOR MATCH NO. 1

ROUND ONE

TEAM A
A1: The Police Force
A2: A Griffin
A3: Ever Ready
A4: Lord Darnley (Henry Stuart)

TEAM B
A1: British Medical Association
A2: A bee
A3: Generous
A4: Chou En-Lai

ROUND TWO

TEAM A
A1: Skaro
A1: Sir Francis Drake
A3: Dr. George Carey
A4. Mark Twain

TEAM B
A1: Mars
A2: Arizona
A3: Ronald Runcie
A4: Harry

ROUND THREE

TEAM A
A1: The George Cross
A2: Schnorbitz
A3: Essex
A4: Jim Bergerac

TEAM B
A1: Abyssinia
A2: The Corrective Party
A3: North Yorkshire
A4: The Ardennes

ROUND FOUR

TEAM A
A1: Fay Weldon

A2: Wards
A3: British Army on the Rhine

A4: Jennifer Capriati

TEAM B
A1: The Fur Trade (killing
    animals for their fur)
A2: Theakstons
A3: The Honourable Artillery
    Company
A4: Australian

ROUND FIVE

TEAM A
A1: General Motors
A2: July (15th)
A3: The Bislett Games
A4: Hergé

TEAM B
A1: Mitsubishi/Renault
A2: Winchester
A3: Mary Decker
A4: Botswana

ROUND SIX

TEAM A
A1: University of Manchester
    Institute of Science &
    Technology

TEAM B
A1: Massachusetts Institute of
    Technology

A2: Wisconsin

A3: 14th Century

A4: Inverness

A2: Maryland

A3: 10th Century

A4: April

ROUND SEVEN

TEAM A
A1: "Sing Little Birdy"

A2: Mary Hopkin ("Knock Knock Who's There?")

A3: "Power To All Our Friends"

A4: France

TEAM B
A1: The Allisons

A2: Izhar Cohen (and Alphabeta), and Milk and Honey

A3: Three – France, Spain, Holland

A4: Four – Sandy Shaw, Lulu, Brotherhood of Man, Bucks Fizz

FINAL ROUND

TEAM A
A1: Greece

A2: Somerset and Gloucestershire

A3: The Basque Separatist Movement – ETA

A4: Three times ('58, '62 and '70)

TEAM B
A1: Olympic Airways

A2: Durham and Yorkshire

A3: The Goldfinch

A4: Czechoslovakia

END OF MAIN QUIZ

THE "GALLON" LEG

TEAM A
A1: Benin

A2: Marx and Engels

A3: A writing surface, or canvas, which can be used over and over again.

A4: James Herriot

A5: It was named after the Philistines, who lived there when the tribes of Israel arrived.

A6: Isotherm

A7: Jimmy Connors

A8: A "Los Angelino"

TEAM B
A1: A thick jam made from damsons

A2: The chalice which Christ drank from at the Last Supper

A3: CONVALESCENCE

A4: They are sisters

A5: Judah

A6: Squeeze

A7: James J. Braddock

A8: Lake Superior

A: The Domesday Book

A: Gloucestershire (and, for a short time "London")

A: Denis Wheatley

A: Measuring time with extreme accuracy

SET OF ANSWERS FOR MATCH NO. 2

ROUND ONE

TEAM A
A1: G7 Summits

A2: South African United Cricket Board

A3: Granada

A4: *Anni-frid* Lyngstad

TEAM B
A1: Italy and Canada

A2: £2.9 (two point nine) million.

A3: The initial letters of the Christian names of the four members

A4: The Crankies

ROUND TWO

TEAM A
A1: West Sussex

A2: The College of Cardinals

A3: Kathy Bates (for her role in the film "Misery")

A4: Bridgewater

TEAM B
A1: Gloucestershire

A2: Miles Coverdale

A3: James Caan

A4: Terylene

ROUND THREE

TEAM A
A1: Friday ("Push Off Early, Tomorrow's Saturday")

A2: Malcolm

A3: Capital Gains Tax

A4: Herod

TEAM B
A1: A toilet (usually outside)

A2: Huron

A3: Gold

A4: Eros

ROUND FOUR

TEAM A
A1: Light Blue

A2: County Tipperary

A3: Rapid Reaction Corps

A4: Whitbread

TEAM B
A1: The Blackwall Tunnel

A2: County Louth

A3: Ronald Searle

A4: Fullers

ROUND FIVE

TEAM A
A1: 1991

A2: Dominoes

TEAM B
A1: 1981

A2: Mah Jong

A3: Alice B. Toklas   A3: Mary Shelley
A4: "All You Need Is Love"   A4: George Harrison

ROUND SIX

TEAM A	TEAM B
A1: Indianapolis	A1: French Communist Party
A2: The work of the Auxiliary Fire Crews in London during the Blitz.	A2: In an aircraft factory.
A3: Companion of the Order of St. Michael and St. George.	A3: Mecca
A4: Zagreb	A4: A (vicious) dog – actually a pit bull terrier cross

ROUND SEVEN

TEAM A	TEAM B
A1: Jonathan Harker	A1: Mina Murray
A2: Carpathians	A2: Whitby
A3: Demeter	A3: A huge dog
A4: Professor van Helsing	A4: Carfax Abbey

FINAL ROUND

TEAM A	TEAM B
A1: Calamity Jane	A1: Florence Nightingale
A2: U.S. Virgin Islands	A2: The study or collection of mollusc shells
A3: Moffat	A3: The town in Grampian, which gave its name to the dish
A4: The Orinoco	A4: Chief of the Imperial General Staff.

END OF MAIN QUIZ

THE "GALLON" LEG

TEAM A	TEAM B
A1: Joe Fagin	A1: Kenny Everett
A2: Michelmas	A2: Government Chief Whip
A3: Rex Harrison	A3: Vanessa Redgrave
A4: Church of Christ, Scientist.	A4: The Church Army
A5: Robert Ulrich	A5: Mancuso (FBI)
A6: In a plane crash	A6: Ranger Guide
A7: Alan Shepherd	A7: Master Sergeant
A8: Ohio River	A8: Rome, 1960

A: Surrounding, or rotating around, the Sun.

A: Ten

A: Church of Jesus Christ of Latterday Saints

A: Nine

SET OF ANSWERS FOR MATCH NO. 3

ROUND ONE

TEAM A
A1: Sir Christopher Wren
A2: Sweden
A3: North Yorkshire
A4: An alloy of copper and nickel

TEAM B
A1: Sir Basil Spence
A2: Belgium
A3: Isle of Wight
A4: Three

ROUND TWO

TEAM A
A1: Shakespeare Memorial Theatre
A2: Kansas
A3: Meryck E. Clifton James
A4: Tunis

TEAM B
A1: New Year's Day
A2: Missouri
A3: Rome and Carthage
A4: Burgundy wine & champagne

ROUND THREE

TEAM A
A1: The Confederate Flag (during the U.S. Civil War)
A2: Ridley Scott
A3: Durham
A4: Norfolk

TEAM B
A1: The Lambada
A2: Wasps
A3: Avon
A4: Jim Bowie

ROUND FOUR

TEAM A
A1: The Royal Naval Reserve (also, certain Yacht Clubs on the Navy List)
A2: Frank Whittle's prototype jet.
A3: Capital Transfer Tax
A4: Eve Pollard

TEAM B
A1: Red and White
A2: Chuck Jeager
A3: Hartlepool United's
A4: Council for National Academic Awards

ROUND FIVE

TEAM A
A1: 14th Century

TEAM B
A1: 13th Century

A2: Gussie Fink-Nottle
A3: The cock
A4: Fifth Avenue

A2: The Drones
A3: Something to do with light
A4: Lexington Avenue

ROUND SIX

TEAM A
A1: "Jilted John"
A2: A rabbit (when cooked)

A3: Copper
A4: None

TEAM B
A1: Horst Jankowski
A2: A liquid lunch (i.e. a can of beer)
A3: The Sikhs
A4: John Simpson, CBE (of the BBC); Martin Nicholson, OBE (of ITN)

ROUND SEVEN

TEAM A
A1: Christabel and Sylvia

A2: Purple; White; Green

A3: Planting a bomb in Lloyd George's house
A4: Representation of the People Act

TEAM B
A1: Women's Social and Political Union
A2: Attempting to present a petition to King George V
A3: Emily Davison

A4: Twenty One

FINAL ROUND

TEAM A
A1: Alan Bleasdale
A2: ETYMOLOGICAL
A3: Lisa Opie
A4: Draco

TEAM B
A1: "L.A. Law".
A2: EUCHARIST
A3: Martine le Moignan
A4: Cygnus

END OF MAIN QUIZ

THE "GALLON" LEG

TEAM A
A1: Coco Chanel
A2: John Betjeman
A3: The Netherlands
A4: James Brown
A5: Glamis Castle
A6: Silver
A7: Fred Truman
A8: Romulus (not Remus)

TEAM B
A1: Marilyn Monroe
A2: Wilfred Owen
A3: The USA
A4: Del Shannon
A5: Clarence House
A6: "For Gallantry"
A7: Dinah Sheridan
A8: The patricians

SET OF ANSWERS FOR MATCH NO. 4

ROUND ONE

TEAM A

A1: British railways before 1923 when all the independent railways were amalgamated into the Big Four

A2: Ben Jonson

A3: Nicholas Winterton

A4: 1911

TEAM B

A1: It was the number designated by the LNER to the record breaking steam engine "Mallard"

A2: John Webster

A3: Keith Vaz

A4: In an air crash, lost in the Arctic Ocean, attempting to rescue Nobile

ROUND TWO

TEAM A

A1: 93

A2: Larry Parnes

A3: Sarah

A4: A fungus (edible toadstool)

TEAM B

A1: Georgie Fame

A2: Isaac

A3: Sooty

A4: Guns 'n' Roses

ROUND THREE

TEAM A

A1: Clive James

A2: Brixton

A3: Edward Elgar

A4: May

TEAM B

A1: General Galtieri

A2: The Battle of Britain, 1940

A3: Richard Chamberlaine

A4: "Open All Hours"

ROUND FOUR

TEAM A

A1: Monica Seles, in 1990

A2: Lord Avebury

A3: Marie Lloyd

A4: The M62 Coach Bombing

TEAM B

A1: Palaeolithic

A2: Antoine Henri *Becquerel*

A3: The Guildford Pub Bombings

A4: Snoring

ROUND FIVE

TEAM A

A1: Clwyd

A2: Robert Preston

TEAM B

A1: Mold

A2: Fleetwood Mac ("The Chain")

A3: The Allman Brothers
("Jessica")

A3: Twice (Horace Lindrum;
Australia; 1952 and Cliff
Thorburn; Canada; 1980)

A4: Stephen Hendry/Jimmy White

A4: Deborah Kerr

ROUND SIX

TEAM A
A1: The Tempest
A2: Fighting Joe
A3: Normandy
A4: July

TEAM B
A1: The Gideons
A2: Northern
A3: It is made from goat's milk
A4: November

ROUND SEVEN

TEAM A
A1: Princess Margaret

A2: Marjorie Antrobus

A3: Detective Sgt. Dave Barry

A4: Heydon Barrow

TEAM B
A1: The SDP (not the Liberal
Democrats)

A2: Peggy Archer (Sid Perks cannot hold the license because he
has a criminal record)

A3: Brian & Jennifer Aldridge, &
family

A4: St. Stephen

FINAL ROUND

TEAM A
A1: The Scottish-English Border
A2: Benzine
A3: It was Norman Scott's
deceased pet, a central
element of Jeremy Thorpe's
conspiracy to murder trial.
A4: Albania

TEAM B
A1: Tenth
A2: Eugene Terreblanche
A3: The Lawn Mower

A4: British Sky Broadcasting

END OF MAIN QUIZ

THE "GALLON" LEG

TEAM A
A1: December 6th
A2: The American PGA
Championship
A3: Insider trading; he was one
of the four prosecuted for
fraud in the Guinness trial
A4: Gibbs SR Toothpaste
A5: 15th Century

TEAM B
A1: December 26th
A2: Franz Beckenbauer

A3: Christendom

A4: Marc Bolan
A5: 19th Century

A6: Radio Forth

A7: Noel Coward

A8: Thomas Cook

A6: Inverness

A7: Sir David Lean

A8: Churchill

SPARE ANSWERS

A: Ancient Rome

A: The Christmas tree

A: Lilian; Jennifer; Tony

A: The Sol

SET OF ANSWERS FOR MATCH NO. 5

ROUND ONE

TEAM A

A1: Malta

A2: Fairy Penguin

A3: Saudi Arabia

A4: Juan Manuel Fangio

TEAM B

A1: An orchestra conductor

A2: Aberystwyth

A3: Baseball

A4: A rabbit (or rabbit skin)

ROUND TWO

TEAM A

A1: "Coronation Street'

A2: A nut

A3: Aaron

A4: A monkey

TEAM B

A1: "Casualty"

A2: Croatia

A3: A fable

A4: Rachel

ROUND THREE

TEAM A

A1: Spain, in the 18th Century

A2: Sergeant Lewis

A3: Disney

A4: White & (Light) Blue

TEAM B

A1: Ruth Rendell

A2: Seven O'Clock

A3: Douglas MacArthur

A4: The Acropolis

ROUND FOUR

TEAM A

A1: Aberdeen

A2: Factoring

A3: Bryan Brown

A4: Deer Hunting

TEAM B

A1: Fairbanks

A2: Mohammed

A3: Rex Harrison

A4: Mary Robinson

ROUND FIVE

TEAM A

A1: Denmark

A2: The Fabians

TEAM B

A1: Dublin

A2: Aix la Chapelle (Aachen)

A3: The U.S.A.
A4: "Brain of Britain"

A3: Steve Backley
A4: The near side

ROUND SIX

TEAM A
A1: Young Men's Hebrew Association
A2: A marine snail (shellfish)
A3: Poetry (also, Scottish Nationalism!)
A4: Barcelona

TEAM B
A1: World Council of Churches
A2: In the blood
A3: Manuel de Falla
A4: West Ham

ROUND SEVEN

TEAM A
A1: "The Apostles"
A2: "Maurice/"Basil"
A3: Sir Stewart Menzies
A4: Intelligence Liaison Officer in Washington

TEAM B
A1: Harold Macmillan
A2: 1951
A3: Beirut
A4: By Cross Channel Steamer, from Southampton

FINAL ROUND

TEAM A
A1: The Ivory Coast
A2: Duncan (The First)
A3: A herb (a plant)
A4: Mid Glamorgan

TEAM B
A1: Pakistan
A2: Macduff
A3: Horse
A4: White

END OF MAIN QUIZ

THE "GALLON" LEG

TEAM A
A1: Ali Akbar Rafsanjani
A2: Newfoundland
A3: Héloise
A4: Togo
A5: Erich Maria Remarque
A6: Tommy Burns
A7: Edward the Seventh
A8: Fairground Attraction

TEAM B
A1: The Apocrypha
A2: Vancouver
A3: Gabriel Fahrenheit
A4: Panama
A5: James Jones
A6: James Buster Douglas
A7: William the Fourth
A8: Judge Dread

SPARE ANSWERS

A: A bird
A: Dwarfism

A: India
A: Benin

SET OF ANSWERS FOR MATCH NO. 6

ROUND ONE

TEAM A	TEAM B
A1: Shropshire	A1: Teachers' salaries
A2: Ray Moore	A2: "Lady Windermere's Fan"
A3: Rossini	A3: Mozart
A4: Investigating UFOs	A4: France

ROUND TWO

TEAM A	TEAM B
A1: Croquet	A1: Ian Baker-Finch
A2: Eindhoven	A2: Sri Lanka
A3: Joao Havelange	A3: A blindfold
A4: New Zealander	A4: Ion Tiriac

ROUND THREE

TEAM A	TEAM B
A1: The Yellow River (Yangtze)	A1: Cycle racing
A2: Oil	A2: Belize
A3: Belgium	A3: A Blue Flag
A4: A cheese	A4: Rice

ROUND FOUR

TEAM A	TEAM B
A1: New York	A1: Ohio
A2: Goa	A2: Bombay
A3: Belgium (because so many wars have been fought there)	A3: Barbados
A4: The George Cross	A4: Blue

ROUND FIVE

TEAM A	TEAM B
A1: David Lean	A1: Angela Lansbury
A2: Annette Mills	A2: "Doogie Howser M.D."
A3: Denis Weaver	A3: JAKKI
A4: Napoleon The Fourteenth	A4: Mud

ROUND SIX

TEAM A	TEAM B
A1: Adam Smith	A1: The Shogun's
A2: Quebec	A2: Montcalm

A3: Carthaginian
A4: The Anglo Dutch Wars

A3: Scipio (Aemilianus)
A4: Chatham

ROUND SEVEN

TEAM A
A1: White
A2: They crash out – totally exhausted?
A3: Three weeks; or 21 days of racing
A4: Bernard Hinault (in 1985)

TEAM B
A1: Team Time Trials
A2: The best hill climber
A3: The pack of cyclists riding together
A4: Eddy Merckx/Jacques Anquetil

FINAL ROUND

TEAM A
A1: The Sun
A2: Quinine
A3: Aries
A4: Mercury

TEAM B
A1: Red – Blue – Green
A2: Saturn
A3: Cancer
A4: Minerologist

END OF MAIN QUIZ

THE "GALLON" LEG

TEAM A
A1: They were built by a man called A.V. Roe
A2: Bananarama
A3: Switzerland
A4: Because they eat shrimps – which exude a pink dye into the flamingos' bodies
A5: Mozambique
A6: Troilus & Cressida
A7: Nato
A8: The Simplon Tunnel (12 miles 500 yards)

TEAM B
A1: Distress
A2: Palm Court Orchestra
A3: Taiwan
A4: Workers are female; drones are male
A5: A ship's deckhouse, usually containing the galley
A6: Hamlet
A7: Shires
A8: The Severn Tunnel (4 miles 628 yards)

SPARE ANSWERS

A: Sir Walter Raleigh
A: William Blake

A: Bournemouth
A: Sinn Fein

ROUND ONE

TEAM A
A1: Mikhail Gorbachev
A2: Do not dry clean
A3: Australia
A4: Rigsby (in "Rising Damp")

TEAM B
A1: William Golding (in 1983)
A2: Cut here
A3: The U.S.A.
A4: Don Warrington

ROUND TWO

TEAM A
A1: St Thomas Aquinas
A2: A crochet
A3: Golf
A4: Size 42

TEAM B
A1: St. Leonard
A2: A semibreve
A3: Fijian
A4: Size 38

ROUND THREE

TEAM A
A1: Robert Robinson
A2: Jackie Stewart
A3: Cambodia (Kampuchea)
A4: Aniseed

TEAM B
A1: Brigitte Bardot
A2: Sixty
A3: The Immune System
A4: The Friends of John McCarthy

ROUND FOUR

TEAM A
A1: Poet Laureate
A2: Derby County
A3: One piece takes another
A4: Pennsylvania

TEAM B
A1: William Wordsworth
A2: Brighton & Hove Albion
A3: Good Move!
A4: Virginia

ROUND FIVE

TEAM A
A1: Literature
A2: Mumm Champagne (Seagram) Accept either
A3: T-shaped
A4: Tom Courtenay

TEAM B
A1: "Midnight's Children"
A2: Newquay
A3: Diagonal
A4: Susan Hampshire

ROUND SIX

TEAM A
A1: France (at Albertville)
A2: The River Tees

TEAM B
A1: Canada (at Calgary)
A2: The River Ribble

A3: Bill Owen

A4: The first four are about God; The last six are about social behaviour

A3: Barry Took

A4: Exodus, (also in Deuteronomy, accept either)

ROUND SEVEN

TEAM A
A1: Rex Hunt

A2: June (14th)

A3: To demolish a whaling station

A4: Major General Jeremy Moore

TEAM B
A1: April (2nd)

A2: Richard Luce/ Humphrey Atkins

A3: Rear Admiral John Woodward

A4: Alexander Haig

FINAL ROUND

TEAM A
A1: "My Left Foot"

A2: Piccadilly

A3: Loud

A4: Brecon Beasons

TEAM B
A1: "Driving Miss Daisie"

A2: Metropolitan or District

A3: Getting progressively louder

A4: The Peak District

END OF MAIN QUIZ

THE "GALLON" LEG

TEAM A
A1: Canis Major (The Great Dog)

A2: Village People

A3: The Mausoleum of King Mausolus

A4: A dog

A5: BRITANNIA

A6: Enniskillen

A7: "Girls Talk"

A8: Henry III

TEAM B
A1: Southern Cross (Crux Australis)

A2: Dan Ackroyd and John Belushi

A3: The Colossus

A4: A sheep

A5: PERSONNEL

A6: Downpatrick

A7: "Nothing Compares 2 U"

A8: Hotspur (or Harry Hotspur)

SPARE ANSWERS

A: Sir Thomas Gresham ("Gresham's Law")

A: Murder (exceeds both cancer and heart disease as cause of death)

A: 200 miles

A: The Actors' Studio

ROUND ONE

TEAM A
A1: November
A2: A goat
A3: International Whaling
    Commission
A4: Yellow

TEAM B
A1: Forty
A2: Tuberculosis
A3: Anaconda

A4: Blue

ROUND TWO

TEAM A
A1: Terry Fields
A2: Frank Zappa

A3: Nigel Kennedy
A4: "Liberty"

TEAM B
A1: Dave Nellist
A2: "The Fifth Man" (in the
    Burgess-MacLean-Philby spy
    saga)
A3: Controller of Radio Three
A4: "Relate"

ROUND THREE

TEAM A
A1: A computer (database)
    program
A2: Luton Town
A3: Queen Elizabeth I
A4: Gas Mark Six

TEAM B
A1: Fulham F.C.

A2: Orange
A3: Thirteen
A4: Hops

ROUND FOUR

TEAM A
A1: Ice Hockey
A2: Bob Beamon
A3: Sandown; Kempton Park;
    Epsom
A4: Lotus

TEAM B
A1: Squash Raquets
A2: Paul Thorburn
A3: Twice (1978 and 1986)

A4: Rowing

ROUND FIVE

TEAM A
A1: Cannon and Ball
A2: Orson Welles/Warren Beatty
A3: Eamon Andrews
A4: The R.A.F.

TEAM B
A1: "Dear John"
A2: "Reds"
A3: Andy Crawford
A4: The Salvation Army

ROUND SIX

TEAM A	TEAM B
A1: Glasgow	A1: St. Paul's Cathedral ("Great Paul")
A2: Barnsley	A2: Borders (just over 100,000 people)
A3: The New Forest	A3: Southend on Sea, Essex
A4: King George the Fifth	A4: William (I) The Conqueror

ROUND SEVEN

TEAM A	TEAM B
A1: India	A1: Northern Ireland
A2: Australia	A2: Bedford
A3: Jeremy John Durham	A3: Jane
A4: Geneva (The United Nations)	A4: 1988

FINAL ROUND

TEAM A	TEAM B
A1: Working with lepers	A1: Madame Curie (for physics in 1903 and chemistry in 1911)
A2: Leona Helmsley	A2: Jean Marie Le Pen
A3: Richard M. Nixon	A3: Ivan the Terrible (Ivan IV)
A4: Baron Brougham	A4: Malcolm X

END OF MAIN QUIZ

THE "GALLON" LEG

TEAM A	TEAM B
A1: Nought point six (0.6)	A1: Five
A2: The Mulberry Bush/The Tavern in the Town	A2: Robinsons
A3: Woburn Abbey	A3: Rossini
A4: A desert dush storm	A4: On gold or silver
A5: Oscar Wilde	A5: 212 degrees
A6: Mexico	A6: Sting
A7: Daphne du Maurier	A7: John Fowles
A8: Uruguay	A8: Mongolia

SPARE ANSWERS

A: George Gershwin	A:	American music/musictrade newspapers
A: The Mansion House	A:	Flax

ROUND ONE

TEAM A
A1: Alison Fisher
A2: The Scilly Islands
A3: Australia
A4: "Open All Hours"

TEAM B
A1: Liz McColgan
A2: London
A3: Sir Ian McKellan
A4: Twenty Four

ROUND TWO

TEAM A
A1: Green (pale yellowish-green)
A2: Austria and Hungary
A3: Hanging first – Trial afterwards
A4: Jupiter

TEAM B
A1: Alderney and Herm
A2: France and Russia
A3: An aviatrix (or aviatrice)
A4: Earl Marshal

ROUND THREE

TEAM A
A1: Gramophone records
A2: 131 (144 minus 13)
A3: Durex (their main brand name for sticky tape)
A4: Birmingham

TEAM B
A1: Sproggett & Sylvester
A2: Delirium Tremens
A3: Kent
A4: Eccles (Eccles cake)

ROUND FOUR

TEAM A
A1: Veterinary Surgeon
A2: Donald Budge
A3: Resembling, or to do with, skin
A4: Elvis Costello

TEAM B
A1: Maureen (Little Mo) Connolly
A2: Barts (St. Bartholomews)
A3: Alma Cogan
A4: Clear plastic, like perspex

ROUND FIVE

TEAM A
A1: Four
A2: Lewes
A3: The Haka
A4: Eamon de Valera

TEAM B
A1: William Butler Yeats
A2: Mars and Neptune
A3: Humberside
A4: The Sutton Hoo Burial Ship

ROUND SIX

TEAM A
A1: Gary Player
A2: "Everything But the Girl"

TEAM B
A1: Boxing (Jack Dempsey)
A2: Jackie Trent

A3: Gibbs Mew

A4: A semi-precious stone (the national stone of Norway!)

A3: Brakspeare's

A4: The interior of an oyster shell

ROUND SEVEN

TEAM A

A1: In the Pacific Ocean

A2: John Tracy (Space Monitor)

A3: "Thunderbirds FAB – The Next Generation"

A4: Thunderbird Four (the submarine)

TEAM B

A1: International Rescue

A2: "Thunderbird Six"

A3: The Hood

A4: Appollo astronauts

FINAL ROUND

TEAM A

A1: 1960

A2: John Travolta

A3: Faust (or Faustus)

A4: Ocean Sound

TEAM B

A1: 1963

A2: Invicta Radio

A3: Flora

A4: David Hemmings

END OF MAIN QUIZ

THE "GALLON" LEG

TEAM A

A1: Dudley

A2: Godfather Part II

A3: Roger Uttley

A4: Zoological Society of London

A5: Carrick Roads

A6: A lunatic smashed it to smithereens.

A7: Spain

A8: Gregory Peck/Audrey Hepburn

TEAM B

A1: Aladdin

A2: The Arsenal

A3: Trawlerman (Sea fishing)

A4: Lady Ghislaine

A5: Isle of Sheppey

A6: Cremona

A7: Ecology

A8: H.G. Wells

SPARE ANSWERS

A: Dan Hartmann

A: A piece of wood or metal used to repair faulty workmanship

A: Gwent

A: Rugby Union (Springbok)

ROUND ONE

TEAM A	TEAM B
A1: The Litas	A1: Estonia
A2: Africa	A2: Amsterdam
A3: Royal Liver Building	A3: Red (with white borders)
A4: Staffordshire, Warwickshire, Worcestershire	A4: Tyne & Wear

ROUND TWO

TEAM A	TEAM B
A1: Edward Elgar	A1: Gaetano Donizetti
A2: Derek & The Dominoes	A2: Billy Fury
A3: Woodwind	A3: A half-tone
A4: Hank Wangford	A4: Roxette

ROUND THREE

TEAM A	TEAM B
A1: "Flyfishing" by J.R. Hartley	A1: Jimmy Carter
A2: "A Whiter Shade of Pale"	A2: Seven
A3: A North Sea Oil Accommodation Rig	A3: "Blue Suede Shoes"
A4: Two	A4: Lake Lucerne

ROUND FOUR

TEAM A	TEAM B
A1: "The Rose Tattoo"	A1: "The Hobbit"
A2: T.S. Eliot	A2: Four Quartets
A3: Voltaire	A3: "The Last Tycoon"
A4: "The Last of the Mohicans"	A4: Oscar Wilde

ROUND FIVE

TEAM A	TEAM B
A1: 1987	A1: 1982
A2: Their leader was Ned Ludd	A2: An Artist
A3: Bank Holidays	A3: York
A4: Ulyanov	A4: Petrograd

ROUND SIX

TEAM A	TEAM B
A1: "Woman's Hour"	A1: "Acorn Antiques" (Victoria Wood: As Seen on TV)
A2: Stefan Dennis	A2: Nicky Campbell

A3: Fred Dibnah	A3: "Butterflies"
A4: Paul Gascoigne (she is Anne Marie Gascoigne)	A4: Tom Baker

ROUND SEVEN

TEAM A	TEAM B
A1: St. Frideswide	A1: Merton College (in 1264)
A2: New College	A2: Matthew Arnold
A3: Pitt Rivers Museum	A3: Frank Cooper
A4: River Cherwell	A4: Jericho

FINAL ROUND

TEAM A	TEAM B
A1: Runcorn	A1: Three times ('34, '38 and '82)
A2: Ireland	A2: Foinavon
A3: Since 1991. The Horse Racing Board.	A3: Derby County
A4: Wigan Athletic	A4: Peter Roebuck

END OF MAIN QUIZ

THE "GALLON" LEG

TEAM A	TEAM B
A1: Trapper John	A1: Peter Sallis
A2: INTERMEDIARY	A2: ABYSMAL
A3: 1616	A3: 1957
A4: "Tom's Midnight Garden"	A4: Nemesis
A5: Strontium	A5: 990
A6: A rose	A6: St. Vitus
A7: 200 dollars	A7: The Milk Marketing Board
A8: Upper Volta	A8: Greenland

SPARE ANSWERS

A: Black	A: O'Dowd
A: Reading Gaol	A: Northern Territory

SET OF ANSWERS FOR MATCH NO. 11

ROUND ONE

TEAM A	TEAM B
A1: Saudi Arabian	A1: Marmaduke Hussey

A2: Bradford

A3: Wholemeal Flour

A4: He (or she) is insane

A2: Leonard Bernstein

A4: A haddock

A4: A sausage

ROUND TWO

TEAM A

A1: An offshore island (in Scotland)

A2: Fred Davis

A3: Doris Lessing

A4: Gladys Aylward

TEAM B

A1: Sir John Ross

A2: Manchester United (in 1993)

A3: Paul Scott

A4: Anne Frank

ROUND THREE

TEAM A

A1: Sagittarius

A2: Louis XIV (14th) of France

A3: Davy Crockett

A4: The Domesday Book

TEAM B

A1: Bob Holness

A2: Libra

A3: Nutwood

A4: It describes the "humerus"

ROUND FOUR

TEAM A

A1: Hamlet

A2: "How Green Was My Valley"

A3: The planks overlap

A4: Newcastle to Carlisle

TEAM B

A1: William Randolph Hearst

A2: The Peak District

A3: Ten minutes

A4: List Processing

ROUND FIVE

TEAM A

A1: Henry Shrapnel

A2: St. Stephen

A3: Cumbria (2591 sq. miles)

A4: The Rugby League

TEAM B

A1: Thomas Sheraton

A2: 26th December (Boxing Day)

A3: Tresco

A4: England and Scotland

ROUND SIX

TEAM A

A1: Mauritius

A2: Nine (the actual Queen piece, plus all eight pawns if they become promoted)

TEAM B

A1: The one on the back row to the extreme left of the player.

A2: Radio Clyde

A3: Northern Ireland (Belfast) A3: Mount Horeb (The Mountain of God)

A4: Zedekiah A4: Portia

ROUND SEVEN

TEAM A
A1: Rolf Harris's "Two Little Boys"
A2: Cockney Rebel
A3: Van McCoy
A4: K.C. & The Sunshine Band

TEAM B
A1: The Slits
A2: Sarah Brightman
A3: Mr. Boe (a harmonicist)
A4: Pink Floyd's "Another Brick In The Wall"

FINAL ROUND

TEAM A
A1: The Duke of Monmouth

A2: "The Music Man"
A3: Greenall Whitley
A4: The brightness of a star

TEAM B
A1: The Jacobite Army, led by Viscount Dundee
A2: "Funny Girl"
A3: Boddingtons
A4: Sirius

END OF MAIN QUIZ

THE "GALLON" LEG

TEAM A
A1: Tam Dalyell
A2: Peterborough United
A3: Eric Clapton
A4: The Schilling
A5: The nose
A6: Apollo
A7: "The Mummy"
A8: "King Lear"

TEAM B
A1: Gladstone
A2: Alan Price
A3: The Lev
A4: Saturday
A5: Champion
A6: Vishnu
A7: Spiderman
A8: The Mock Turtle

SPARE ANSWERS

A: Spring tide
A: A Zulu spear

A: A jackal
A: Dooley Wilson

SET OF ANSWERS FOR MATCH NO. 12

ROUND ONE

TEAM A
A1: Moldavia
A2: Suffolk (Lowestoft)
A3: Deep Purple
A4: Polo

TEAM B
A1: Bessarabia
A2: Gloucestershire
A3: The Isley Brothers
A4: Athletics

ROUND TWO

TEAM A
A1: Carbon
A2: Wiltshire
A3: My fault; I am to blame

A4: The denier

TEAM B
A1: Silicon
A2: Canada
A3: In wine, the truth, (or "wine loosens the tongue")
A4: Real Estate, Buildings

ROUND THREE

TEAM A
A1: Blenheim Palace
A2: Queen Elizabeth II
A3: Sotonian
A4: St. Bruno

TEAM B
A1: D
A2: Pat Garrett
A3: St John the Divine
A4: Wonder Woman

ROUND FOUR

TEAM A
A1: The Lotus Eaters
A2: Alfred Dreyfus
A3: Buffalo (Bison)
A4: 1984

TEAM B
A1: Gloucester
A2: Drogheda
A3: W.L. MacKenzie-King
A4: 1982

ROUND FIVE

TEAM A
A1: Quarter Master, or Steersman, or Helmsman
A2: Carlisle United
A3: Steering Mechanism
A4: Thomas Hardy

TEAM B
A1: Glass blowers

A2: Aston Villa
A3: Spear side
A4: Arthur Hugh Clough

ROUND SIX

TEAM A
A1: Bob Ford
A2: "A Hard Rain's Gonna Fall"

TEAM B
A1: St. Sarah
A2: "Somethin' Else" (Eddie Cochran)

A3: Felixstowe
A4: The Valkyries

A3: Virginia/North Carolina
A4: Woden (Odin)

ROUND SEVEN

TEAM A
A1: "Casino Royale"
A2: Special Executive for Counter-Intelligence, Terrorism, Revenge and Extortion
A3: "The Spy Who Loved Me"
A4: "Moonraker"

TEAM B
A1: 4½ litre Bentley convertible
A2: "The Man With The Golden Gun"
A3: "You Only Live Twice"
A4: Death to Spies

FINAL ROUND

TEAM A
A1: Swimming (a particular stroke)
A2: Dvorak ("New World" symphony)
A3: St. Pancras (Euston Road)
A4: "Gardeners' Question Time"

TEAM B
A1: Caesar (meaning King)
A2: Karl Orff ("Carmina Burana")
A3: British Museum
A4: "Poldark"

END OF MAIN QUIZ

THE "GALLON" LEG

TEAM A
A1: Milan
A2: Meat or Veg cut into very thin short strips
A3: Oliver Cromwell's
A4: Monkeys have tails; apes do not
A5: Suva
A6: World Cancer Research Fund
A7: John Huston
A8: Speedway

TEAM B
A1: Frankfurt
A2: Dolly Varden
A3: Charles Wesley
A4: 1930 (accept five years either way)
A5: Queen Elizabeth II
A6: British Heart Foundation
A7: Kathy Gale
A8: Sunderland

SPARE ANSWERS

A: Fleet Street
A: Sussex

A: Tommy Docherty
A: William Peter Blatty

SET OF ANSWERS FOR MATCH NO. 13

ROUND ONE

TEAM A	TEAM B
A1: Durham and Sunderland	A1: Morpeth
A2: Liverpool Street	A2: Primrose Hill
A3: Inner Hebrides	A3: Tobermory
A4: Portland	A4: Studland Heath

ROUND TWO

TEAM A	TEAM B
A1: RHYTHM	A1: CATARRH
A2: A money lender	A2: A raspberry
A3: In private, or in secret	A3: "Id est"
A4: It sheds its horns	A4: Fylfot

ROUND THREE

TEAM A	TEAM B
A1: The rupee	A1: Treatment of disease by chemical means
A2: Greece and Turkey	A2: William Tell
A3: An area of land reclaimed from the sea in the Netherlands	A3: Twenty Four
A4: Col. Robert Baden-Powell	A4: A fear of the Chinese

ROUND FOUR

TEAM A	TEAM B
A1: "Erasure"	A1: Iceland
A2: Claude Debussy	A2: Aaron Copland
A3: George Harrison	A3: Norwegian Wood
A4: Dance of the Sugarplum Fairy (from Tchaikovsky's "Nutcracker Suite")	A4: Handel's "Water Music" (the hornpipe suite)

ROUND FIVE

TEAM A	TEAM B
A1: Little fleas (to bite them)	A1: Death
A2: Samuel Pepys	A2: William Wordsworth
A3: A dog	A3: Catch mice
A4: Sir Edward Heath	A4: Anne Robinson

ROUND SIX

TEAM A	TEAM B
A1: McLaren	A1: Chris Tavaré

A2: Ian Knight
A3: George Courteney
A4: A shot which comes off the side wall before hitting the front wall

A2: The four minute mile
A3: Bobby Kerr
A4: A shot which causes the ball to bounce in the crack between the wall and the floor.

ROUND SEVEN

TEAM A
A1: 18th June
A2: Rye
A3: They formed squares
A4: Marshal Ney

TEAM B
A1: Ligny
A2: Lord Uxbridge
A3: La Belle Alliance
A4: The Lion Hill (built as a Netherlands memorial in the 1820s)

FINAL ROUND

TEAM A
A1: Bolivia
A2: Edith Cresson, the French Prime Minister
A3: Hubert Humphrey
A4: Oleg Gordievsky

TEAM B
A1: Ethiopia
A2: Helping George Blake to escape from prison in 1966.
A3: Nelson Rockerfeller
A4: He became the first "Raving Loony Party" candidate to be elected to office

END OF MAIN QUIZ

THE "GALLON" LEG

TEAM A
A1: "Pi"
A2: "Black Bag"
A3: Durham Light Infantry
A4: Flodden Field
A5: The Sea of Japan
A6: Julian Cope

A7: M1
A8: Addis Ababa

TEAM B
A1: The Yellow Spot
A2: Felix
A3: Nancy Mitford
A4: King Henry VIII
A5: Port Moresby
A6: Paula Wilcox and Sally Thomset

A7: Alexander Dumas
A8: Aberdeen

SPARE ANSWERS

A: PNEUMONIA
A: Five

A: Peruvian
A: It was the first railway bridge ever built

SET OF ANSWERS FOR MATCH NO. 14

ROUND ONE

TEAM A
A1: "The Wizard of Oz"
A2: Mother of Pearl
A3: "Ulysses"
A4: ADOLESCENCE

TEAM B
A1: A whippet
A2: The Salvation Army
A3: Pluto
A4: OESTROGEN

ROUND TWO

TEAM A
A1: Victoria
A2: Comptesse du Barry
A3: Two faced; hypocritical
A4: Seven

TEAM B
A1: Bird Cage Walk
A2: King David
A3: Humerous; "funny bone"
A4: The Great Barrier Reef
(128,000 sq. miles in area)

ROUND THREE

TEAM A
A1: Cantons

A2: A kiln for drying hops
A3: Dr. Samuel Johnson
A4: Amy Johnson

TEAM B
A1: The shaven crown of a
(monk's) head.
A2: Six
A3: Constantinople
A4: 200

ROUND FOUR

TEAM A
A1: Darlington
A2: The Denmark Strait
A3: In a pastry case

A4: Norman LaMont

TEAM B
A1: Derby County
A2: The Caspian Sea
A3: Dice (Craps); they are the
bad numbers which led to a
stalemate
A4: "Magic" Johnson

ROUND FIVE

TEAM A
A1: 1981
A2: The Singing Nun
A3: HMS Mary Rose
A4: Matthew Arnold

TEAM B
A1: 1984
A2: Belgian
A3: 126 m.p.h.
A4: Robert Browning

TEAM A	TEAM B
A1: Blake's Seven	A1: Whoopee Goldberg
A2: Christopher Craig	A2: Tiananmen Square
A3: Hampshire	A3: The University Boat Race
A4: DUN LAOGHAIRE	A4: MAGDALEN

ROUND SEVEN

TEAM A	TEAM B
A1: 1962	A1: Cortina was the venue for the Winter Olympic Games
A2: "Consul"	A2: 1200 cc
A3: Cream (white) with a green flash	A3: 1976
A4: "Pinto"	A4: Cortina Crusader

FINAL ROUND

A1: Twice (in '64 and '66)	A1: Aberdeen
A2: Fermanagh	A2: The Jarrow Hunger March
A3: A period of history (with no ruling authority) between Kings or other rulers	A3: Below
A4: "The Man Who Never Was"	A4: Grand Duchy of Fenwick

END OF MAIN QUIZ

THE "GALLON" LEG

TEAM A	TEAM B
A1: Esau	A1: Jacob
A2: A person who collects (studies) moths and butterflies	A2: A seat (or carriage) fixed onto the back of an elephant
A3: The sap of various trees	A3: Opium
A4: Eddie Cochran	A4: Big Bopper/Richie Valens
A5: On your finger	A5: In the brain
A6: G.K. Chesterton	A6: J.M. Barrie
A7: Washington D.C.	A7: Granada
A8: Oxford	A8: Mary, Queen of Scots

SPARE ANSWERS

A: Daily News	A: Tattershall Castle
A: In the carburetter	A: Jacob's Ladder

ROUND ONE

TEAM A
A1: Kenneth Wolstenholme (in the dying seconds of the 1966 World Cup Final)
A2: Hereward Radio
A3: Court of Session
A4: Percy Faith

TEAM B
A1: Wrestling
A2: Radio Broadland
A3: Either Joe Loss or Laurie Johnson or Ted Heath
A4: An instrument for measuring the skull

ROUND TWO

TEAM A
A1: Tennesee
A2: Church Warden
A3: Richard Wilson
A4: Ascot

TEAM B
A1: New Mexico
A2: "One Foot In The Grave"
A3: Cirencester
A4: Paul Warwick

ROUND THREE

TEAM A
A1: Nebuchadnezzar
A2: Cardinal Basil Hulme
A3: Hail Mary
A4: Lead and Tin

TEAM B
A1: In good faith; with honesty
A2: Alexander the Great
A3: Churchill and Roosevelt
A4: The Schneider Trophy

ROUND FOUR

TEAM A
A1: When it is furthest from the Sun
A2: The 8.15 from Manchester
A3: Lord Byron
A4: Being the leading amateur

TEAM B
A1: When it is furthest from the Earth
A2: Leslie Crowther
A3: Royal St. George's, Sandwich
A4: Poetry. (A tiny verse form — just seventeen syllables long)

ROUND FIVE

TEAM A
A1: Brief Encounter
A2: Carmarthen
A3: Government Communications Head Quarters
A4: Middlesbrough

TEAM B
A1: Dyfed
A2: Rachmaninov
A3: Formula Translation
A4: Juventus

ROUND SIX

TEAM A
A1: Ghana
A2: CATERWAUL
A3: George Michael
A4: Surrey

TEAM B
A1: Turkey
A2: EPHEMERAL
A3: Elvis Presley
A4: Derbyshire

ROUND SEVEN

TEAM A
A1: Lord High Admirals Regiment
A2: 1704 (July)

A3: Hannah Snell
A4: Battle of Belle Isle

TEAM B
A1: Portsmouth – Plymouth – Chatham
A2: Napoleon (on his way to exile)
A3: Bunker Hill
A4: "Les Petites Grenadiers"

FINAL ROUND

TEAM A
A1: Perseus
A2: Two
A3: Baseball
A4: Church of the New Jerusalem

TEAM B
A1: Cassandra
A2: Four
A3: Crewe Alexandra
A4: Queen Anne

END OF MAIN QUIZ

THE "GALLON" LEG

TEAM A
A1: Edith Cresson
A2: A commentary on the Bible, which provides the entire civil and religious law
A3: The Woodstock pop festival
A4: Australia
A5: The Orange/The Zambesi
A6: Highland
A7: Baking Powder/Water
A8: Five Shillings

TEAM B
A1: Italy
A2: Bank of Commerce and Credit International

A3: South Kensington
A4: Literacy
A5: The Gallic Wars (58–51 BC)
A6: Ipswich
A7: Two Shillings
A8: The kidneys

SPARE ANSWERS

A: Bethlehem (Bedlam)
A: The A66

A: The Yukon
A: E.M. Forster

SET OF ANSWERS FOR MATCH NO. 16

ROUND ONE

TEAM A
A1: The Fleet Prison
A2: King Charles The Second
(1651)
A3: Eddie Charlton
A4: Joy Adamson

TEAM B
A1: Elizabeth Garrett Anderson
A2: "Not proven"

A3: O.J. Simpson
A4: Janis Joplin

ROUND TWO

TEAM A
A1: Gordon Strachan
A2: The Manifesto of the
Communist Party
A3: Ankara, in Turkey
A4: "Thunderball" (Also in the
film "Never Say Never
Again")

TEAM B
A1: Oldham Athletic
A2: German

A3: Stephen Foster
A4: Dr. No

ROUND THREE

TEAM A
A1: Whales
A2: Queen Elizabeth II Bridge
(i.e. Dartford M25 Bridge)
A3: Jilly Cooper
A4: British chemist/physicist

TEAM B
A1: Shinto
A2: Flushing Meadow

A3: Michael Farraday
A4: The Baltic Sea

ROUND FOUR

TEAM A
A1: Bolivia or Paraguay

A2: Oatmeal (oats)
A3: Brian Boru
A4: The Isle of Wight Steam
- Railway

TEAM B
A1: Australia (Northern
Territory)
A2: Journalists (writers)
A3: King Henry The Second
A4: The Bluebell Line, in Sussex

ROUND FIVE

TEAM A
A1: "Edelweiss" in 1967
A2: The Caribbean Sea
A3: The Undertones
A4: Florida

TEAM B
A1: Mr. Pastry
A2: Antarctica
A3: Major
A4: Watford FC

ROUND SIX

TEAM A	TEAM B
A1: The Gulf of Bothnia	A1: "Don't Go Breaking My Heart" (They are the real names of Elton John and Kiki Dee)
A2: Mary Norton	A2: Norway's
A3: "Thou shalt not bear false witness"	A3: New Hampshire
A4: Finland	A4: The Piccadilly Line

ROUND SEVEN

TEAM A	TEAM B
A1: Montenegro; Macedonia; Bosnia	A1: Red White and Blue
A2: Belgrade	A2: Skopje
A3: Albanians	A3: Chetniks
A4: King Peter (the second)	A4: Dubrovnik

FINAL ROUND

TEAM A	TEAM B
A1: Michael Stich	A1: Liz McColgan (in the 10,000 m)
A2: "A Farewell To Arms"	A2: David Nobbs
A3: Runnymede	A3: The Cairngorms
A4: Beans	A4: A gluten-free diet

END OF MAIN QUIZ

THE "GALLON" LEG

TEAM A	TEAM B
A1: The M2	A1: The M8
A2: A biscuit	A2: The Magpie
A3: William (1) The Conqueror	A3: Ratatouille
A4: Twenty Seven	A4: The Revelation (of St. John)
A5: Oliver Goldsmith	A5: Arthur Ransome
A6: Pegasus	A6: Bow Wow Wow
A7: The Dail (pronounced "doyle")	A7: Brutus
A8: "Casino Royale"	A8: Thetis

SPARE ANSWERS

A:	Harold Macmillan	A:	The Prime Minister
A:	"Help!"	A:	The pound

THE MARTELL/RNLI QUIZ LEAGUE
YOUR QUESTIONS ANSWERED

WHY HAVE A QUIZ TEAM? Team quizzes are fun, and involve not only the actual contestants, but everyone who is watching. As the quiz season progresses, you will find that the team can build up quite an enthusiastic following. This league is played on those quiet winter evenings when your "local" might otherwise be empty!

HOW MANY PEOPLE DO YOU NEED? Each team needs five members for each quiz night – four to play in the team, and a fifth person either to ask the questions (at home matches) or be scorer (at away matches). Don't worry if occasionally you can't get all five people together on match nights. At a pinch, you can usually get by with less, and there are always willing volunteers to sit in at short notice. You don't need to register a squad of players, so you can chop and change your team as often as you like.

WILL IT INVOLVE A LOT OF TRAVELLING? No. Although this is a national competition with a prestigious national prize to be won, the Leagues are all local, involving teams from other pubs and clubs near you.

WHO IS GOING TO PLAY IN THE LEAGUE? Each league is made up of eight teams, which may be from pubs or social clubs. You can enter two teams in the league, if you have enough enthusiastic quizzers on hand.

HOW LONG DOES THE LEAGUE LAST? Fourteen weeks – from late October through to February (with a three week break over Christmas). Each team plays seven home matches and seven away matches.

WHAT NIGHT OF THE WEEK IS THE QUIZ PLAYED? Mondays. All the teams in the National Martell/RNLI Quiz Leagues around the country play on Monday evenings, using the same questions simultaneously.

The starting time is 8.30 p.m., and the quiz usually takes about an hour and a half.

WHAT HAPPENS AT THE END OF THE SEASON? A complete list of League winners and runners-up and scores is published nationally, and the League winners are each presented with a handsome framed Champions Certificate.

WHO GOES TO AINTREE? Four of the highest-scoring League winners from around the country are invited to participate in an end-of-season *Champion of Champions* play off in Liverpool, on the evening before the Martell Grand National, as part of a all-expenses-paid weekend at the Aintree race meeting. The teams invited to Aintree in 1994 will be the two highest-scoring League Champions, the highest-scoring first-time League Champion, and the highest-scoring League Champion playing in the competition for the first time.

WHAT DOES THE "LOCAL CO-ORDINATOR" DO? He, or she, distributes the sealed sets of questions weekly to the home venues, and compiles a record of results, so that all the teams in the League can see how the League season is progressing. The "local co-ordinator" is the link between the participating teams and the national organisers. Without a local volunteer co-ordinator, the league would not be able to function. Each league's co-ordinator receives from Martell a large complimentary bottle of Cognac for their trouble!

CAN WE VOLUNTEER TO BE THE "LOCAL CO-ORDINATOR"? Yes, please do. Without a local co-ordinator, your league cannot progress. Just tick the special box on your entry form.

IS THIS A NEW COMPETITION? No, the National Martell/RNLI Quiz League has been running since 1990, and is now in its fourth successful season. Each year the competition involves more teams than ever.

WHO COMPILES THE QUESTIONS? They are specially compiled for the League by Wise Owl Quiz Promotions, in Poole, Dorset. None of the questions come from other quizzes, so there is no conflict with other games or competitions.

ARE THE QUESTIONS DIFFICULT? Any question is difficult if you don't know the answer! However, this competition covers a broad range of General and Specialist Knowledge subjects, including many popular topics such as TV, films, pop music and sport.

DON'T YOU HAVE TO HAVE A VERY CLEVER TEAM TO MAKE IT WORTH PARTICIPATING? No, your team will enjoy the competition no matter how good or bad they are. Many of our teams who had low expectations at the beginning of the season ended up doing well, and thoroughly enjoying every week's match.

HOW MUCH DOES IT COST TO ENTER THE LEAGUE? In 1993–1994 the cost was £30 for the 14-week season. That's under fifty pence per person per match. All the entry money goes to the RNLI – none of it is spent on administration or other costs. The RNLI is a Registered Charity which depends entirely upon voluntary contributions to maintain the Lifeboat Service, which costs £48 million a year.

WHAT HAPPENS IF THERE AREN'T ENOUGH TEAMS IN OUR AREA TO MAKE UP A LEAGUE? You money will be refunded in full if we cannot make up a viable league in your locality.

WHEN WILL WE HEAR IF OUR LEAGUE IS TO GO AHEAD? The recruiting period ends on August 31st each year, and fixture lists and league team lists are issued during September.

DO WE HAVE TO BE A MARTELL CUSTOMER TO BE IN THE QUIZ? Yes, your pub or club premises have to be a Martell stockist, but then (just like every lifeboat) every bar carries a bottle of Martell Cognac, doesn't it?

HOW DO WE ENTER? Complete the enquiry form and send it to Wise Owl Quiz Promotions, P.O. Box 327, Poole, Dorset BH15 2RG immediately. You will be sent by return a full information pack for the current or forthcoming season.

CAN YOU EXPLAIN ONE MORE THING FOR US? Of course! Simply telephone Freephone 0800 212574 or Fax 0202 736191 for further information.

QUIZ LEAGUE SEASON
ENQUIRY FORM

TEAM NAME ....

VENUE FOR HOME MATCHES ....

ADDRESS ....

.... POST CODE ....

TELEPHONE NUMBER ....

CONTACT (Landlord, Team Captain, etc.) ....

Signed .... Date ....

PLEASE STATE IF YOU OR YOUR TEAM CAPTAIN WOULD BE WILLING
TO ACT AS YOUR LEAGUE'S LOCAL CO-ORDINATOR: Yes/No

The League Competition commences every year on the last Monday in
October. League placings are usually confirmed in September. The fixture lists, rules and other pre-season information are distributed during September.

Send or fax your enquiry to Wise Owl Quiz Promotions,
P.O. Box 327, Poole, Dorset BH15 2RG.
Telephone: Freephone 0800 212574   Fax 0202 736191

How your Membership helps the Lifeboat Crews.

For over 160 years Britain's lifeboat crews have been putting to sea to save lives.

And today, as in 1824, we still rely entirely on voluntary contributions.

Which is why your membership is so vital to us.

Without your help, and that of thousands like you, there wouldn't be a lifeboat service.

Counting the cost.

It costs a staggering £130,000 per day to run Britain's lifeboats.

To keep a single lifeboat running at full speed takes £1 for 1½ minutes.

(And remember that, on average, a lifeboat is called out every 2 hours, every day of the year.)

Our aim in 1993 is to progress our 3 year plan to replace older and slower boats with modern ones at an overall cost of £24 million.

Looked at another way, we need over thirty new members to kit out just one lifeboatman in protective gear, because it costs more than £300 per man.

And with 210 lifeboat stations around Great Britain, The Channel Islands and the Republic of Ireland, the task is, quite simply, immense.

The people who never count the cost to themselves.

Selfless devotion to the service and undeniable bravery, have marked out lifeboat crews throughout our history.

Their skills and courage, given voluntarily, have resulted in over 122,000 lives saved since 1824.

They are prepared to put to sea in terrifying conditions and are on call 24 hours a day, 365 days of the year.

Consider also that almost a third of rescues take place in darkness and you'll begin to understand the qualities of Britain's lifeboatmen and women.

What you'll receive as a member.

Joining us means you'll receive our quarterly magazine 'Lifeboat'. In it you'll find facts about the service, stories of recent rescues and profiles of the people involved. It also keeps you abreast of fundraising activities and the many social events organised nationwide.

You'll also receive details of the RNLI insignia (badges, flags, ties, etc) which you can buy.

Young people have the opportunity to join our Storm Force scheme. They'll receive a special magazine with various posters, badges and stickers to collect.

Most importantly, you'll also know that your membership has actively helped to support this vital service. And for this you'll receive our thanks. Join us today.

Royal National Lifeboat Institution, West Quay Road, Poole, Dorset BH15 1HZ.
Tel: Poole (0202) 671133.

Royal National Lifeboat Institution

Reg. Charity No. 209603.